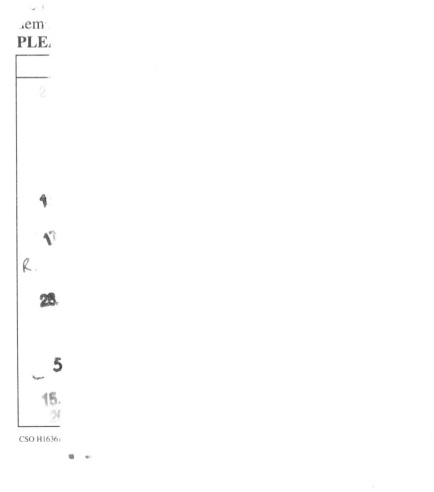

em

PLE

2

4

1

R.

28

5

15

CSO H1636

GOING BACK

Written by Wendy Grant

In collaboration with Frederick Brayshay

Best Wishes
Wendy Grant

FOR PAM

First published in the United Kingdom in 1992
by Eastbrook Publishing, Trull, Taunton, Somerset, England.

ISBN 0 9518812 0 5

Cover illustration by Tony Thornhill.

Printed and bound by J H Haynes & Co Ltd. Sparkford, England.

CONTENTS

INTRODUCTION

It wasn't until my closest friend Pam died that I came to spend any length of time with her husband, Fred Brayshay. Together we recalled her incredibly vital personality, her capacity for living and enjoying all things, her sense of humour - we both agreed that nothing and no one was ever going to replace her.

For both of us it was a necessary time of healing and coming to terms with the reality of her no longer being with us. As we talked and walked and sometimes sketched or painted together I became aware that Fred too, in his very individual way, had a personality and character that intrigued and fascinated me.

I think it was that moment one day when he casually remarked, 'Do you know, Wendy, I've even slept in a dog kennel', I realised he had a story worth telling and that I wanted to record it.

Born in a workhouse, put in an orphanage, adopted, rejected, evacuated, reclaimed, rejected - so his story unfolds. By the age of thirteen he had been placed in seven different institutional homes.

His experiences could have turned him into a bitter negative man, but he has maintained a sense of humour and an ability to deal with life philosophically that is both humbling and awe-inspiring. He also has the gift of being able to recall with great accuracy many happenings, customs, and a way of life lived in North Yorkshire and the Midlands that no longer exists.

The day Fred finally obtained his birth certificate he knew he had to go back and discover his roots. He felt compelled to find out if he had any blood relatives and why he had been abandoned.

He was to discover that his 'goings back' revealed truths that were stranger than fiction. The coincidences that arose making this story complete are quite remarkable. For Fred it became a going back, going back and going back again.

Contrary to the general belief that all institutional homes and regimented patterns of behaviour destroy individualism, Fred emerges as an unique human being. He adamantly declares that the final 'home' he lived in was the best thing that ever happened to him during his formative years.

When you ask someone to tell you of a past personal experience you usually obtain a factual report often unconsciously embellished to entertain or hold the attention of the listener; but when you enquire as to what they could actually smell when this event was happening, the texture of the material beneath their fingers, the taste and sounds involved in that experience, then you lead the person all the way back to that time and they are actually there again, using all the senses that make it come alive.

So it was with Fred. When, for example, he recalled returning from his failed search in Leeds and found himself in the Earnshaw's farm yard, he smelled again the evocative smell of the paraffin lamps and felt the texture of the straw against his hands and knees as he crawled into the dog's kennel for protection against the night - when he rose next morning and ate the chips he had been too tired to finish the night before, he could taste again the cold congealed fat in his mouth and feel it against his teeth. He was **there** and it was happening to him.

As a hypnotherapist, it was possible for me to help Fred go back in time and recall with accuracy and honesty the past he sought to unravel.

This is essentially Fred's experiences, memories and feelings as HE recalls them from going back; sometimes physically, often by allowing his mind to re-enter the past. Only on about two occasions did he find it impossible to remember the name of the person involved and here I have taken the liberty of inventing one in order to write of those occasions; where we thought exposure might offend the individual concerned we have altered the name.

The final information obtained after this story had been completed is included at the end of the book under the heading 'In Conclusion'. We felt it was important that you should be given the up-to-date details of The Children's Society and its work, what happened to Mr Dawson who had such a profound influence on Fred as a young man, and the final effect on Fred and his family brought about by his persistence in 'Going Back' and exposing the truth.

Alive, dramatic, cruel, poignant, funny, his story unfolds. Be prepared to laugh and perhaps even shed a tear for that little boy he re-discovers: be prepared for a few surprises.

Fred said, 'Write me down as a nobody, just an ordinary man.' This then is the extraordinary story of an ordinary man.

Wendy Grant March 1992
Member of the National Association of Hypnotists and Psychotherapists

DIARY OF EVENTS

Frederick Brayshay

18 Sept 1928	Born in a Workhouse Ripon
28 Dec 1928 to 30 May 1930	St Christopher's Home For Babies Leeds
1930 - 1938	Cliviger/Holme Chapel with adoptive parents
1938 - 1939	St George's Home For Waifs and Strays Salford Manchester
1939 - 1941	Evacuated to Fleetwood/The Old Military Hospital and then The Old School House (The Testimonial School)
April 1941 to June 1942	Returned to adoptive parents in Brockenhurst Street, Burnley
July 1942	Three weeks in Buckley Hall, Rochdale
July 1942 to Jan 1945	Standon Farm Industrial School Staffs
1945 - 1946	Apprenticed to Lotus Shoe Co. Staffs.
1946 - 1948	Army - Malaya
1948 - 1953	Returned to Lotus & then Staffordshire Council
1953 - 1956	Travelled and met Pam
1956 - 1958	Worked in the South of England
1958	Married Pam
1958 - 1964	Lived in King's Cross, worked in London
1964 - 1975	Lived in Romford, worked in London
1976 - 1991	Lived and worked in Somerset where he currently resides

PROLOGUE

His shoes squeaked slightly as he crossed the tiled floor, the distance he had to walk to reach the carpeting seemed interminable. Conscious of his surroundings, as if seeing them for the first time, he noted the cream washed walls, the ugly modern office furniture, the distant sound of telephones ringing. Sunlight spilled in through the window making strange patterns across a woman's head as it cascaded down on to her desk.

'Mr Brayshay? Mr Frederick Brayshay?' She looked at him, a smile playing on her lips.

Of course she knew who he was, but he supposed she had to verify it - part of the job. But she was a nice woman, she actually behaved as if she cared, though God knew how she could, doing the same job day after day.

He wondered for a moment whether she ever speculated on the outcome of her involvement in other people's lives. It must be a funny feeling, though not half as funny as the feeling he was now experiencing as he sat down on the chair and faced her; it was an empty feeling and yet, somewhere in the middle of him a flutter of excitement rose, slowly intensifying, taking hold of his throat, tightening the vocal cords so that his words come out strange, almost alien to his own ears.

'Yes, I'm Fred,' he said. He tried to smile back. 'But then you know that already.'

'Yes, but we must follow procedure - just to make sure there's no mistake. I have some good news for you.'

She seemed to expect a response but there wasn't anything he could think of to say.

After hesitating for a moment she continued, 'Do you remember ever hearing your mother's name?'

'I...I always thought it was Mary.' Why did he say that? He didn't know. He hadn't the slightest idea, but the name had always remained with him, a sort of label he could put on his past.

She was fingering the piece of paper on her desk. He was glad to see her nails were clean, unvarnished, although it would have been better if no one had touched it - if in some way it could just have been given to him without any other human contact. But that was ridiculous. He was grateful to all of them - the man from the Adoption Office who had put him on to the Registrar, those who had made telephone calls, written letters - and this woman here, Mrs Goodwin, representative of the Registrar of Births and Deaths.

What was it she was saying? He realised she was repeating something. 'Actually her name was Elsie. Elsie Tew.'

'Ah!' So his memory hadn't completely fooled him. He had always known the name Tew belonged somewhere in his past.

She lifted the slip of paper, hand outstretched she offered it to him. 'Good luck, Mr Brayshay. I hope that it helps.'

He stared at it. It should have been faded, yellowing, with the dry feel of crackling old paper between his fingers.

'It's only a copy, of course,' she reminded him.

'Yes, of course.' He stood up, feeling the sun on his face, almost like a blessing. Now he was getting fanciful - stupid really, a grown man like him ready to burst into tears because some stranger hands him a piece of paper. 'Well, thanks a lot.'

'I'm afraid we have to charge you.'

'Oh yes. Sorry, I forgot.' He fished in his pocket. A few coins - the price of his past. It seemed ironic.

A wedding, just completed, prevented his exodus from the premises. As he tried politely to push his way through the mass of people all desperately intent upon celebrating, on getting themselves included in the photographs, he heard snatches of their jokes and observed the almost hysterical gaiety. He was struck by the tone of the whole proceedings; everyone seemed to have a cigarette either hung from their lips or streaming smoke from their fingers. The groom was very dark skinned, almost black in fact, he looked somewhat incongruous standing there beside the bride so pale and undernourished.

I'm not a snob, he thought, but I don't like this. It was somehow so seedy, the very antithesis of all he now held precious. A powerful thought temporarily rooted him to the spot: This could never have been part of my background. We may have been poor by today's standards, but we weren't like that.

He didn't know what made him feel so strange about it. He wished they hadn't been there, somehow they sullied his experience. He wanted to find a quiet corner of his own where he could pause and look for a long time at that piece of paper, savouring the feelings, trying to make sense of what it all meant to him.

Outside he sat on a bench isolated in his own little pool of silence as people, like ants, walked past unheeding.

Here am I, on the verge of the most incredible journey of my life, and no one else cares a damn. He still held the paper in his hand. In a minute he'd put on his glasses and read it. He'd waited so long, there was no thought of turning back now. He **had to know.**

Funny he hadn't pursued it earlier. Oh, there was that time back in the seventies when he'd visited Richmond and Cliviger, seeing again the place where he'd spent his early childhood, and Holme Chapel where he'd gone to school; then there had been that day when he'd run away to Leeds... He now recognised that he had never earnestly pursued his real parentage, his **real** beginnings; he'd been without the drive then or the intention he now felt compelling him to follow through to the end - or rather the beginning - wherever that might prove to be.

Somehow though, when Pam had been alive, there hadn't been that driving urge to discover his roots. He acknowledged there had always been a feeling, but it had been more like a 'something I'll do one day' kind of feeling. But with Pam he hadn't needed that reassurance of who he was, where he had come from. She had filled his life; Pam and the children. But now Pam had gone - God how he missed her! And the children were grown up, all doing their own thing.....

Slowly he pulled his spectacle case from his jacket pocket and placed the glasses on his nose. The words seemed suddenly to jump out at him. A birth certificate couldn't lie. He was the son of Elsie Tew. Domestic servant. Date of birth, 18th of September 1928. Today, he realised, was the 11th of September 1990. It was almost sixty two years to the day - if he'd left it until next week he'd have been celebrating his birthday on the day he actually got his birth certificate.

He read on: Place of birth, 75, Allhallowgate, Ripon. Father unknown.

Part of the Poor Law Infirmary where Fred was born which was within the Ripon Workhouse

10

The main building of the Workhouse Ripon

Born in a workhouse! It didn't exactly say that, but he knew. He could picture the building, though how that was possible he had yet to find out.

Memories came sylph-like into his mind, a snatch of one, a flash of another, and now a solid one binding them together. Somewhere a large goose figured, and there he was running off with his Dad's bicycle and sleeping in a dog kennel.

Oh yes! over the years he'd sometimes thought about things and wondered about his **real** parents, where his roots were; there had been over-heard snatches of conversations, half-suggestions he was never quite sure were actually directed at him or part of his past; and once, long ago, his adoptive father had told him he had fetched him from Leeds when he was a tiny baby.

He read again the address in Ripon. So his secretary Vera had been right, the details she'd dug up for him in back in seventy six after he failed in his abortive search in Richmond proved right. But Ripon had no Registrar on the day of his visit and they'd sent him here to Harrogate - still, it wouldn't take long to get back. It obviously made sense to start there.

So, he mused, he now had confirmation that originally he'd been called Tew. Having the name made all sorts of things possible; for one thing he could get a ten year passport which wasn't available to people who had no known place of birth.

He sighed deeply, he could go back to the area where he was born, surely there must still be people around who would remember - perhaps he even had relatives

11

there. He wondered what they would say when he knocked on the door. 'I'm Fred,' he'd say. 'I believe we're related.'

Away from the city, driving along leafy lanes where autumn colours competed with each other in their extravagant display, Fred found his mind slipping back to that other time he had made his search.

The year had been 1976. He supposed it came about because he and Pam had been thinking of leaving London and moving down to the West Country. He was involved in one of the biggest undertakings of his career, managing the building of the Army and Navy redevelopment at Victoria. Yes, he felt proud of that. But commuting each day through streams of endless traffic between there and his home in Romford had made him see what a 'rat race' life had become. It was time to get out.

Before I go, he thought, I'd like to take a look at Richmond in North Yorkshire. Somehow I've had the thought for a long time that that place has something to do with me and my history. One thing's for sure, Pam won't want to come with me.

He knew she wasn't interested. Pam lived in the present, she completely failed to understand why he needed at all to go back anywhere. But then Pam had had a family. And a father, by God! who could scare the pants off you if you let him. He hadn't been in the Metropolitan Police Force for nothing!

I'll mention it to Arthur Banks, Fred decided. Perhaps he'd like to come with me, we could make it into a bit of an outing. We can have a pint or two along the way, maybe even stay overnight somewhere.

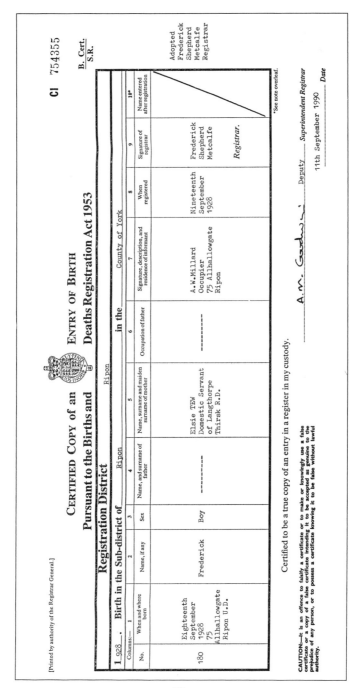

[Printed by authority of the Registrar General.]

CI 754355

CERTIFIED COPY of an ENTRY OF BIRTH
Pursuant to the Births and Deaths Registration Act 1953

B. Cert.
S.R.

Registration District Ripon

1928. **Birth in the Sub-district of** Ripon **in the** County of York

No.	When and where born	Name, if any	Sex	Name, and surname of father	Name, surname and maiden surname of mother	Occupation of father	Signature, description, and residence of informant	When registered	Signature of registrar	Name entered after registration
Columns:— 1	2	3	4	5	6	7	8	9	10*
180	Eighteenth September 1928 75 Allhallowgate Ripon U.D.	Frederick	Boy	————	Elsie TEW Domestic Servant of Langthorpe Thirsk R.D.	————	A.W.Millard Occupier 75 Allhallowgate Ripon	Nineteenth September 1928	Frederick Shepherd Metcalfe *Registrar.*	Adopted Frederick Shepherd Metcalfe Registrar

*See note overleaf.

Certified to be a true copy of an entry in a register in my custody.

A. W. Goodwin .... Deputy ...... *Superintendent Registrar*

11th September 1990 .... *Date*

CAUTION:—It is an offence to falsify a certificate or to make or knowingly use a false certificate or a copy of a false certificate intending it to be accepted as genuine to the prejudice of any person, or to possess a certificate knowing it to be false without lawful authority.

13

Chapter 1

FOOL'S ERRAND

1976

The more he thought about it, the more the idea tickled Fred's imagination. He'd see what his pal Arthur Banks thought of going with him up to Yorkshire. It couldn't do any harm to just take a look.

Arthur grinned. 'Bloody good idea, Fred. I could do with getting away for a day or two. Course I'll come. Not that you couldn't just as easy make the trip without me. But... well, I suppose in your place I'd like a bit of moral support. You never know what you might turn up.'

Arthur had done all the driving. Fred, sitting beside him felt the tension growing. He was like a kid going on holiday.

Richmond proved to be a typical North Country town. The problem they had trying to park almost made them give up and turn back, and then trying to find the registry office - well, you'd have thought no one ever got born, married or died in that town.

As they finally entered the morbid building Arthur said, 'I'll say this for you, Fred, you're a persistent bugger once you set your mind to something.'

'Let's hope they haven't lost their records, I wouldn't put it past them. The whole place feels like it could do with a good shake up.' Fred grinned, masking the weird feeling he was getting in his stomach.

But there was nothing, though they searched diligently. No boy child was recorded having been born and registered there on September 18th 1928. Nothing had been quite such a let-down.

Wandering around church yards, thumbing through church records, wading through books in the library, the truth slowly dawned - his past did **not** start in Richmond, he was in the wrong place.

'I feel a bloody fool,' he admitted to Arthur. 'I always had it in my mind that my mother's name was Mary and she'd lived in Richmond.'

'Well, you reckon you were adopted when you were only a baby, so how the hell could you be expected to remember?' Arthur gave him a thump. 'Come on, Fred, it's back to the drawing board.'

Fred turned to face him, oblivious of the people edging past him on the pavement. He tried to weigh up how Arthur was feeling about the whole thing. Was he bored? Would he go along the way a bit further?

'Arthur?' He had to ask. 'Could we stop off at Low Bradley near Skipton, it's on the way to Burnley? I know **that** won't be a fool's errand. That's where relatives of my adoptive father lived. I spent some of my holidays there. They were happy times. I...I'd like to take a look.'

Maybe it was the note of longing in Fred's voice, the feeling of nostalgia he transmitted to his friend, or maybe Arthur didn't want yet to return home to the responsibilities, the relentless routine - in any case he nodded saying, 'Let's give it a try then.'

As they walked back to the car Fred attempted to communicate to Arthur some of his enthusiasm. 'It's a lovely village, a few miles from the town if my memory serves me right. A real typical Yorkshire village. I shouldn't be surprised to find it hasn't changed a bit. It was one of those timeless places you occasionally come across.'

They drove over the moors, becoming aware of the hovering mists, the bleakness; it was a strange disembodied kind of experience.

'Reminds me of Wuthering Heights,' Fred said. 'You either love it or hate it. I must have loved it for right now all my memories seem to be happy ones.'

For a while they travelled in silence. There was so much to see, so much to think about.

Fred looked at the clock on the dash board. 'The light's going. We'd better pull off if we can find somewhere for the night. It's best we arrive there in the daylight.'

He was quiet for a few minutes and then said, 'The Brayshay family was strong there. I can remember Ted Brayshay who used to have the butcher's shop, he was my adoptive Dad's brother. I wouldn't mind betting someone from his family's still around. But it's no use going when the shop's closed.'

They found a grey stone building offering accommodation and went inside. There they talked and ate and downed a couple of pints deciding to make an early night of it and move on immediately after breakfast next morning.

It ought to have made an impression. He felt he should have recorded a rich verbal description of the place, but as it receded into the distance Fred realised it had no meaning for him at all. His mind, his whole being was ahead where Bradley awaited him, where the echoes of his childhood rang amongst the hills and down in the valley. Bradley where some of his earliest memories began.

Suddenly Fred shouted, 'Look! There's Swales' farm. I used to stay there.'

Arthur sighed quietly. At least he'd found something he could put his finger on. He hoped for Fred's sake there'd be more, but he knew only too well how things changed and how one's memory can play tricks.

Swale's Farm Bradley Yorkshire

There certainly wasn't a parking problem. They left the car and wandered around the tiny village. It didn't take long.

On the outskirts they could see a big development of houses. 'Wimpey,' said Fred in disgust. And then, resignedly added, 'Still, I suppose people have to live somewhere.'

But the village itself with its stone cottages, rows of terrace houses, the old chapel and farm buildings was still the same. And there was the old wool mill still working. Ah! And over there the butchers, just as he remembered it, and opposite the little pub were Ivy Cottages - that's where his adoptive father's brother Uncle Teddy with Aunt Hilda and their children had lived. He had spent so many happy hours there. He saw suddenly before him a vivid picture of himself sitting up at their kitchen table drawing and reading comics.

'Do you know, Arthur,' he declared, 'I can even remember being there when the first issue of the Radio Fun came out.'

Arthur laughed. 'That dates you, Fred!'

Fred squared his shoulders, wishing he didn't feel quite so much like a school boy on his first day at a new school. 'Come on, Arthur,' he said. 'We'll pay a visit to that butchers. Let's see what we can find out.'

16

Ivy Cottages Bradley Yorkshire

He looked up at the sign over the doorway. J BRAYSHAY BUTCHER. It was a most peculiar feeling, seeing the name written there, just as if nothing had changed in more than fifty years.

The instant he stepped over the mat-well into the shop he knew he hadn't made another mistake: Jim Brayshay, nephew of his Dad, stood there, a large white apron across his stomach, running a carving knife over a sharpening steel. He looked up. 'Yes, gentlemen. Can I help you?'

Fred smiled. 'You're Jim Brayshay, aren't you?' he asked.

'That's right?'

'I'm Fred. You'll perhaps remember me as Freddie Brayshay...I was John Airey's son...I used to stay on the farm with the Swales. You must remember me. I stayed with your family many a time.'

The man hesitated. 'Well, I remember John Airey sure enough. So...you're Fred.'

He didn't seem very interested though. Perhaps he'd thought he had new customers moving into the area, or he was just plain uninterested in someone else's past.

'Don't you remember me?' Fred's eyes searched his face.

'Yes, I suppose I do. What can I do for you?' But there was no welcome in his

17

voice, no hint of interest.

A terrible sense of disappointment engulfed Fred. What had he expected anyhow? There wasn't any reason why the man should welcome him with open arms - the way he probably saw it Fred was simply a stranger making claims that went back too far - claims that had no meaning to him in the middle of a busy working day.

'I was in the district,' Fred half-lied. 'Just thought I'd look up a few people, see what had happened to them.'

Jim Brayshay shook his head. 'Most of 'em have moved on or passed on. It's bin a long time. Fifty years or more I reckon.'

Fred leaned forward across the counter ignoring the half pig lying there. 'Do you know what happened to my father? Is John Airey still alive? I lost touch with him after my marriage. He was a sick man then I recall, he'd had a couple of strokes.'

'Now I can tell you that,' Jim's voice brightened. 'I'm not very likely to forget. I was due to go to his funeral. I'd just got a brand new car. I only opened the door for a minute and a bloody lorry came hurtling by and smashed into it. So I never did get there. And this driver tried to say it was my fault...'

Fred stepped back. 'We'll be off then,' he said. 'Thanks for your time.'

He didn't wait to hear anymore. He felt totally discouraged. The way he saw it, the man was only too eager to elaborate on what had happened to him and his car, he wasn't the least bit interested in what had happened to his uncle or in knowing Fred. The irony of the meeting left a bitterness; perhaps it was because he was not 'real' family or, as he'd always suspected, people were only interested in themselves.

Outside Fred lifted his head, squared his shoulders and walked back to the car. Then, with a tenacity bred from years of working to get things done he said to Arthur, 'Let's get out of here. We're going to Burnley. At least I am. What do you say?'

Arthur rattled the car keys. 'I guess we're in this together, Fred. You navigate and don't bloody get us lost. I don't want to sleep the night in a fog in the middle of the moors on the back-seat of this car.'

As they drove away from Bradley Fred consulted the map. 'That's funny,' he said thoughtfully. 'Cliviger has disappeared, it doesn't appear on the map. Still, it makes no difference, Walk Mill is here - it's the same place.'

Note: Although Walk Mill was the village, Cliviger was the parish - in fact at one time it was the largest parish in England and owed its emergence to the Cliviger Coal and Coke Company - the people of Burnley thought that Walk Mill was Cliviger and the name Walk Mill was rarely used.

'It was Cliviger near Burnley that I was taken to when I was adopted,' Fred said. 'I lived there till I was about seven. I can remember it clear as anything. And that's where we're going now.' He rubbed the glass with his sleeve and peered through the windscreen.

Arthur let out a sigh. 'Okay, Fred, you're the boss.'

While Arthur drove Fred looked around him searching for familiar landmarks. He could hardly contain the excitement welling up inside him. He fidgeted on the seat, wanting to tell Arthur to put his foot down, then wanting to ask him to slow down so that he could savour the very moment they came over the hill and saw the village lying before them.

'You'll see the pit and the big black wheel any moment now,' Fred breathed. 'And right next to it there's the cotton mill with its tall chimney where my adoptive father used to work. There's a row of...' His voice faded as he stared in disbelief. 'They...they've gone! The pit, the mill, the chimneys...they've disappeared.'

View of Cliviger as it was in Fred's day

Cliviger as Fred found it when he returned.

He stared at the landscaped valley where the most impressive buildings of his young life had once stood.

Arthur looked at him, noting the shocked expression, the tightly clenched hands. 'Still want to go on?' he asked gently. 'You could be in for some more shocks?'

'Yes, carry on.' Fred sat up straight. 'I was never a man to quit - especially having got this far.'

As they dropped down into the tiny village he gave a cry of recognition. 'There's the terraced houses.' And then: 'My God! How they've changed! They're a row of mews cottages now. Would you believe it?'

They drove up and down the village staring at the buildings and the streets which after so long were still surprisingly familiar to Fred. His eyes caught the glitter of water - it was the River Calder with all its poignant memories.

'What now?' Arthur wanted to know. It was approaching midday and he was feeling thirsty and hungry.

'There's a pub called The Gordon Lennox,' Fred told him. 'Funny name for a pub. Look! There it is. You can park over there. Come on. I'll buy you lunch.'

They bought two pints of beer and ordered steak and kidney pies with mushy peas. The tap room lady, looking all of seventy years, approached the round polished wood table. And just as he remembered it, she wore a pouch over her dress that had to date back to Victorian times; he recalled how in the old days the 'bar ladies' used to take money from the customers as they did the rounds, coming to the tables rather than waiting for the customer to approach the bar, placing the money in the pouch. And here she was, wearing the very same kind of pouch he had seen so many times as a child, still doing the same old routine.

He bought her a drink. He could have hugged her - despite the moth-eaten grey dowdiness of her dress, the pockets of wrinkled brown skin that made up her face half hidden by a muddle of wispy hair - to hear her say that she recalled him being brought there as a baby; it was the first real evidence that he had existed in this place and it hadn't been some quirk of his imagination that had got it all wrong.

As she stood polishing glasses she told him: 'Yes, your adopted mother's name was Grace - Grace Mary Brayshay. To tell you the truth there was more than one of us at that time thought as how you were her sister's baby - born out of wedlock, or so we thought, an' she was just puttin' around the story of adoptin' you to cover up the truth.'

She nodded, her wizened face a picture as she turned her eyes this way and that, searching for the memories. 'But your adopted father was a nice man I recall. John Airey Brayshay, though everyone allus called him John Airey. I had a lot of time for him. He thought the world of you.'

21

'I suppose over the years people forgot about the idea of you bein' her sister's nipper,' she went on. 'Then they moved to Holme. I heard some talk that they'd taken a pub there.'

He smiled, delighted that she remembered. There was so much he wanted to ask, things he hoped she could tell him. But it had been too long ago, and her memory, she said with a wry expression, was not as good as it used to be.

'But I know someone as will remember you.' Her face brightened. 'Are you stayin' in the area?'

'We planned to book in somewhere in Burnley for the night,' Fred told her.

'Then you come back tonight,' she instructed him. 'I'll see this person and get him to come in and meet you.'

She refused to be drawn any further, smiling to herself, pleased at her own idea of springing a surprise. It was a long time since anything nearly as exciting had happened to her.

As they left the pub Fred looked at her. 'You won't forget?' he prompted.

'You just come back this evenin'. I'll make sure he comes,' was all she'd say.

It was what Fred called a 'commercial hotel' - the sort of place Sales Reps used. Not too up-market, but it was clean and practical without going 'over the top'.

Eating an early evening meal Arthur asked, 'Do you think the old girl knows what she's doing?'

'Oh, yes! I think she knows very well exactly what she's up to. The thing is, who is this chap? Will he turn up? And do I really want to meet him?'

Arthur dug a knife into his meat. 'We'll find out soon enough,' he said and began to chew stoically on a piece of beef.

Fred saw him first, standing at the bar. He hadn't changed. He recognised him instantly. 'Roy Clarkson!'

The man spun round and looked at him, and Fred could feel the years rolling away between them. Roy, his childhood friend, going right back to infant's school.

'Fred! It is you! Well, I'll be damned! I couldn't believe it when they told me.' His friendly smile beamed at Fred. 'Whatever's brought you back here?'

Fred felt the firm grip of his hand. 'You amongst other things,' he informed him. 'I'm looking for my roots. A journey back into nostalgia you might say.'

He introduced Arthur and they sat down at a table. Roy and Fred simply couldn't stop grinning at each other.

'We were best mates,' Roy told Arthur. 'And we got into some scrapes together.'

'St John's school, Holme,' Fred reminisced. 'That's where we met. It was a church school.'

'Remember Miss Lancaster?' Roy asked.

'Who could forget her! We were all scared of her, but she was a good teacher. They knew about discipline in those days. Didn't do us any harm either.'

Roy said, 'Do you know, Fred, she's still alive.'

Amazed, Fred stared at him. 'Miss Lancaster? Here, in Cliviger?'

'No. She's in the same school house over at Holme where she always was. You ought to look her up. I wonder if she'll remember you?'

'Who else is there? Have they all worn as well as you?' Fred saw before him a man who had spent his whole life in this protected environment, never moving away, never seeing anything of the rest of the world. Perhaps his youthful appearance was accounted for by the fact that he had experienced no stress, no pressure in trying to exist in an alien world.

'You remember my cousin Jack?' he was saying. 'He's in a mental home.'

'I'm sorry to hear that.' But Fred saw in his mind the cousin, and he'd known, all that long time ago, that he hadn't been like the rest of them. Somehow it wasn't a surprise.

'And the ice works have closed. You remember, that's where they made ice, and we'd sneak in and pinch a bit and drop it down the backs of the girl's dresses.' Roy chuckled, lifting his glass once more from the table, drinking deeply. He was a contented man.

Note: Originally the Ice Factory, which still stands, was designed to be used as a brewery. It was of an advanced design, the idea being that water fed by gravity from a spring near Mereclough started at the top of the building, was processed into beer down each successive storey until barrels could be lowered on to drays on the ground floor. The brewery failed because the directors had planned to deliver directly to houses, farms and country pubs, but by the time the brewery was ready to go into production men had taken to drinking in the ale houses or tap rooms and the main brewers, Masseys and Grimshaws, had by then tied up or bought the country pubs so there was no outlet for the beer from Cliviger.

'Are the Clarksons still over at Towneley Lodge?' Fred wanted to know. 'Oh, I recall the hours and hours we spent in the grounds there making our own adventures, hunting everything from dragons to escaped prisoners'.

'It was a splendid place,' Roy agreed. 'Part of the Towneley Hall Museum. Of course most of the people have moved.'

'I'm married you know,' he rattled on. 'Have been for donkey's years. We still live in the village though. We're very happy,' he added with a moving simplicity.

'Remember the stories about the witches of Pendle? I used to be scared stiff in case they really existed.' Fred laughed. 'My, but they were good days! And I haven't forgotten how good your family were to me. Years later I used to walk miles and miles just to be with you all.'

Roy pulled a photo from his pocket.

'What have you got there?' Fred peered curiously at the faded picture. It was a photo of five children, all staring at the camera.

'There you are.' Roy pointed to a tiny round face in the picture.

Fred let out a cry. 'And there's you... and isn't that Christine Sunter?'

The minutes were swallowed up into hours as they laughed and remembered and became serious again.

With great reluctance they rose to leave. 'It's been great seeing you again. Thank's for coming, Roy.' Fred clapped an arm around his shoulders. 'I'll never forget this.'

The next day was the day of the Grand National. As they drove toward Cliviger they listened to the man on the car radio talking about the horses as if he knew each of them personally.

'I'm going to have a few quid on one,' Fred said. 'I'm not missing the Grand National. It might even cover our expenses up here.'

He was out of the car now, staring in disbelief at a row of houses which had very obviously and expensively been transformed. 'Once, when my adoptive father went bankrupt we had to live in one of those,' Fred said. 'They were the pits in those days. Long Row it was called. It felt as if it was just about as low as one could go an' all.'

He threw back his head and laughed, his white hair shining, and for a moment a smile of pure happiness shone in his blue eyes. 'Who'd have believed it?' he said again. 'Now, let's find number three, Industrial Buildings - that's what's on my adoption certificate.'

Note: The correct name was and still is Industrial Buildings, but to the locals it was always known as Tod Co-op.

'That's where I lived,' Fred said with growing excitement. 'Right next to the cotton mill... that was until my adopted mother decided they should buy a pub and Dad left his safe engineering job at the mill. It was never right for him, that pub was doomed to failure. It changed my whole life.'

He gave his head a firm shake. 'Anyhow, that's another story. Let's pay a call on number three now.'

Oh he found the house right enough, and he recalled little Rita Clegg who had lived nearby - everyone had nicknamed them the Terrible Twins - and there was the yard with the houses stacked back to back in two rows, one on either side. That had been his playground.

A powerful feeling surged through him. It left him shaken. Now there was no one... no one to remember.

He could hear the blunt north country accents drifting out of open windows, but they were as a strange tongue, for none called his name, no broom was shaken in his direction, no one was there to yell abuse at him or to threaten him with a good tannin on his backside for some mischievous prank he and Rita Clegg had dared to execute.

'Let's try the Co-op shop,' Fred suggested. He pointed. 'Look! It's still there, at the end of the row of houses.'

He tried a dozen names before he mentioned Rita Clegg.

'Ah, now I do know where she is.' The man behind the till nodded. 'She's moved to Burnley. Here, I'll write it down for you. I don't know if you'll find her in during the day though.'

But Arthur had had enough. Fred couldn't help but notice the way he fidgeted and sighed. Well, he had to admit he'd put up with a lot.

'We'll go back to the hotel,' Arthur said impatiently, 'and you can drop me off. You can find this Rita on your own.'

Fred hadn't forgotten the Grand National. Leaving Arthur he walked into the nearest betting shop in Burnley before going in search of his childhood playmate. He knew all along which horse he was going to put his money on. Rag Trade, owned by Teasy Weasy. Once it was done it was done, he didn't agonise over the results, either he made a quid or two or he lost it. It was more a custom nowadays than anything else.

It was just after lunch when he arrived at her door. There was only one way of knowing who was on the other side or what sort of a welcome he'd get - if any. He pressed his finger on the bell.

There was that moment - oh, so bloody wonderful - when she looked at him and he realised she recognised him instantly. 'You're Freddie!' she said, holding open wide the door. 'Come on in.'

He followed her into a clean, nicely furnished house. Signs of children were evident around the room. She indicated a chair.

'Well, so you've come back,' she said, looking enormously pleased.

She hadn't changed. Her hair showed no signs of grey. She just kind of looked like a bigger edition of the lass he'd played with all those years ago in the yard that ran alongside the houses of the Co-op Buildings.

He told her: 'I hear you've done well for yourself.'

'Sounds very grand, doesn't it?' She grinned, and there behind the well-groomed woman of the world was still the face of the little girl he remembered.

She looked nice. He couldn't think of another word to describe her. It gave him a good feeling, sitting there drinking tea with her, listening to all her news.

'Yes, I married,' he said at last. 'We have three lovely children and I've a smashing wife. There's times I've had to work bloody hard, but it's been worth it.'

Explaining about Arthur he said, 'Why don't we come back later and pick you up and we can take you out to dinner.

He could see she liked the idea. 'About six thirty then?'

'That'll be lovely.'

He walked away, proud to think he could take her out and buy her a meal. He'd treat her to the very best. She was smart in an unpretentious way. Yes, Rita Clegg had done well for herself. It set him wondering about the rest of the youngsters who had once formed such an important part of his life in Cliviger.

His mouth wouldn't stop smiling, he felt so good. They'd shared a few laughs together, reminiscing. Rita was still the same cheerful person he remembered, with fun ready to bubble over.

From a newsagent he bought a copy of the local evening paper and turned to the back page. Rag Trade had crossed the line first. So he'd won enough to buy the finest meal in town. He laughed to himself as he made his way back to Arthur.

'We're meeting her at her house and going on to the St James' restaurant,' Fred told him. 'She's a lovely lady. You'll enjoy meeting her.'

Arthur made an effort to enter into the spirit of things but he appeared a bit subdued. Fred pondered for some time before telling him about his winnings.

'You canny sod!' Arthur's face broke into a smile. 'You definitely can pay for the meal after that.'

They arrived promptly at six thirty. But something had happened. Rita's face appeared round the edge of the door. She very obviously didn't want to let them in.

Her eyes looked dark and distressed.

'Anythin' up?' Fred had always been one to come straight to the point.

'I'm afraid I can't come.'

'You're joking!' But he knew she wasn't.

The voice of another woman reached them as they stood there staring in open mouthed astonishment at Rita.

'It's my friend...' She struggled for words that would explain her change of heart. 'I...I can't leave her. She's a bit...well, er... upset.'

He would have liked to stay and talk, to ask her to confirm more of his fading memories, but he read her expression and knew there was nothing further that could be said. Very clearly she just wanted them to go.

'Well, take care of yourself,' Fred said and turned away.

Driving back, Arthur began to roar with laughter. Tears squeezed from the corners of his eyes. Finally, getting his mirth under control he spluttered, 'You never know what's round the corner. Life's full of surprises isn't it, Fred?'

Fred felt his own face break into a wide smile. To tell the truth he hadn't quite known what to think.

'Well, that's it, Arthur,' he finally stated. 'I'll make a quick call on that old school mistress of mine first thing tomorrow and then we'll start for home. I've found out what I wanted to know. It wasn't so very special after all. But it's helped sort out some things in my head. I've definitely made up my mind, I'm moving the family to Somerset.'

Chapter 2

CHILDHOOD DAYS IN CLIVIGER

It was a long journey back to Romford. Arthur seemed content to drive and listen to the radio. Fred closed his eyes and began to think. He felt himself slipping back through the years, he even felt like he was growing smaller. And then...all of a sudden, he was five years old again, standing outside the school at Holme looking up at the beautiful grey stone building.

'That's it,' his mother said. 'That's St John's School. You'll be alright. There's other children startin' today. No doubt you'll already know some of 'em.' She gave his hand a tug. It felt strange, she wasn't one to hold him or make a fuss.

'Do I just go on in?' he asked. He stared down at his new trousers and black leather lace-up shoes. He wondered who was going to do up the laces for him if he had to take them off. He hoped no one would pinch them.

'Oh, come on,' she said. 'I'll take you in, just this first time. But you're goin' to have to learn to go to and from school by yerself. I can't find the time to keep runnin' after you.'

He stared at the other children. Some went eagerly into the building, others, like him, hung back and you could tell they were new pupils not quite sure what to expect.

In a sort of caged area he was given a peg and told to hang up his coat. He wanted to throw his arms round his mother and ask her to stay for a while, but she hurried away without looking back.

Curiosity finally drove him out into the playground at the back of the building where he found some of the children playing. A group of boys were kicking around a bundle of rags tied up with string.

He thought of his father. He had taken pains to teach him how to write his name. He'd practised over and over again so as not to disappoint him. He'd do anything for his Dad.

His little fingers wrapped around the cool metal body of a tiny toy car. His Dad had made it for him and he felt infinitely proud of it.

Some of the older boys were playing on a wall that edged the yard, pushing their own toys up and down, creating in their imagination a world where buses and cars could achieve anything.

It was exciting really. Buses had only recently begun to appear on the streets. He'd seen them when he went into Burnley on a Saturday with the milk float pulled by Polly sitting beside Mr Butterworth. Mr Butterworth delivered the milk to the people in the town. Some had never even seen a cow, so Mr Butterworth told him. It made him feel real grand sitting up there, especially when the other kids ran after them begging a lift.

Of course he understood that his part of the bargain was to do the running to and fro so that Mr Butterworth, who was suffering from arthritis in his feet, didn't have to keep jumping down off the float.

But the journey with the pony and milk float faded into insignificance as he watched the buses. His Dad had promised him a toy one for Christmas. But it was his birthday in a couple of weeks time. Perhaps he could ask for the bus then. He sighed, his mother had been going on about a new coat and there might not be enough money left over for presents for him.

'Hey, let's have a look?' One of the bigger boys came over. 'Where'd you get it?'

'Me Dad made it.' He said it proudly, holding it out for the boy to admire.

'How could he **make** it?'

'He's an engineer. He can make anything.'

The boy handed it back. 'Want to play?' he asked.

Freddie felt as if his heart would burst. School suddenly seemed a very wonderful place.

Then the bell rang. Everyone rushed to line up. Miss Lancaster, dressed in a long black skirt, stood in the doorway, tall, forbidding.

'All you new children line up at the back,' she said in a voice that expected to be obeyed.

Uncomfortably they shuffled into place. A little girl began to cry.

They marched into a large room, the ceiling seemed a million miles away. Brown wooden desks were placed in rows. The room smelled of ink and polish and chalk dust. Freddie sniffed.

'Don't you have a handkerchief, boy?' She looked at him.

Freddie felt his face turning bright red. He pulled the bit of old sheeting from his jumper sleeve. His mother had roughly sewn it around the edge. He looked up at the school mistress.

'Well, blow your nose.'

Obediently he complied and was then shown to the desk where he was to sit for the rest of his time there. It was all totally beyond his comprehension.

They started with prayers. That was all right, he knew all about praying. His Dad was an ardent church goer and every Sunday morning they made their way together down the road to the Mount Zion chapel.

That first day they played with sand; not out in the playground but right there in the room. He was never to forget the sounds that echoed around the walls - the chalk squeaking across the blackboard, children chanting their tables, the weird chuckling of the stove set in a recess at one end of the room. It was warm and clean and he loved it.

At lunch time they all stopped what they were doing and sat tidily behind their desks eating their sandwiches. Some of the children had only a dry crust of bread with a layer of dripping spread over it. Freddie saw that he had white bread, thinly sliced, and as he peered inside he saw he had meat and pickle. He knew that it was his Dad who had packed them; some time early in the morning before he had gone to work he must have made them for him. Freddie never questioned how he knew, he was just aware instinctively that his mother would never have done them that way for him.

As he sat on his Dad's knee that evening, recounting for him all the things that had happened, he thought: I'm never going to forget my first day at school, not ever.

His Dad gave him a hug. 'I'm proud of you,' he said. 'You did well. But now it's time for bed or you'll never be up and ready tomorrow morning.'

He gave him a piggy-back up the stairs and then stayed to hear Freddie chant his way through his prayers.

Lying in bed, thinking about his day, picturing the playground with its big iron railings, the boys with their cars, the teacher standing at the front of the class wagging her cane at the older boys, he was quite certain that he would never be able to go to sleep that night. It surely had been the most important day of his life.

But sleep in its wisdom stroked his brow and lulled his mind; gradually his eye lids became heavier and heavier - perhaps he'd just close them for a few minutes.....

Each day after school the children walked back to the village in a straggle, the girls whispering secrets, the boys talking about cars and buses and steam trains; running, laughing, falling in a heap on the ash path they would struggle between themselves for something one or other of them had found in the hedgerow.

St John's School Holme Chapel

Pupils of St John's School, Holme Chapel. Fred is standing third from the right in the back row. Roy Clarkson, from whom Fred obtained this photograph in September 1991 is on Fred's right.

31

When the weather was dry they played outside in the courtyard, and when he wasn't with the other children he would sometimes pedal over the cobbles on his tricycle playing his own imaginary games.

He was on his tricycle when Mona Pickles came up to him one day. She was the biggest child in their group. He looked at her, seeing her straight fringe cut severely across the middle of her forehead, shortening her face, somehow narrowing her eyes. Her hair was very dark. She wore a smock and today she had a white apron tied over it. He thought she must be on some errand for her mother.

He stopped his pedalling and stared at her.

'Hello, Freddie.'

'Hello.' He wondered what she wanted.

For a few seconds she was silent, contemplating him. Then, in her blunt North Country voice she announced, 'You know, you'd be quite good lookin' if you wasn't adopted.'

Adopted? He wasn't even sure what she meant. Wasn't she adopted? Weren't all children? Did it mean he was different? He wanted to run inside and ask his Mam, but she'd tell him not to be silly.

He sat there for a long time after Mona had gone trying to remember what it meant to be adopted and why it had happened to him. It was the first time Freddie felt afraid. Even when his mother took the belt to him, which she frequently did when his Dad wasn't at home, he'd never felt like this. It was the way Mona had said it. He realised he didn't like her much - not anymore.

As the weeks went by he got used to the idea. He gradually came to understand what it meant. Was that why his mother never really hugged him? Was that why his Dad was so good to him? He always had time to talk to him, to tell him things and show him how things worked.

It was glorious the day his father made him a kite. All the village came out to watch as they climbed the hill and let the kite go, tugging in its impatient way against the string. And there he was, running for all he was worth, never wanting it to fall out of the sky.

He had fun too with Annie Schofield - all the boys did. She was the only woman they knew who lived all alone. No one knew how she managed with no man to bring home the money. The other women whispered the word 'spinster' as if it was some kind of illness.

'She's a real spinster,' he once heard his mother say. 'Never even had a boy friend. She's not like any of the other women.'

Oh, the pranks they played on her! And how mad she got!

When they could get hold of some cotton and old buttons they'd hang them round the edge of her window, carry the cotton all the way across the road, and then, hiding safely behind a wall or corner, they'd pull on the cotton. Tap, tap, tap. Out she'd come, staring up and down the street with such a puzzled expression on her face. They used to roll on the ground laughing. If she saw them she would come running after them, her big feet flapping. But she never caught them.

Soon it was going to be Christmas again. Only this year it would be different. Miss Lancaster and her assistant Miss Handy had very definite ideas about how the Christmas celebrations were to be organized.

The tree was so big it would hardly go in through the classroom doorway. The children were allowed to hang on its branches the pretty coloured balls and things they had made. There were even wax candles to be lighted on the day of the party.

All the children were making presents for their parents. Cheeks drawn in, intently involved, they concentrated on accomplishing everything in time.

There was to be a special school carol service, and they were putting on plays and a concert. Someone whispered that every single child in the school was to be given a present.

Freddie's eyes were like saucers. He found it difficult to believe the sight of the table, erected on trestles and ladened down with food, was real. And there was a small bag of goodies for each of them to take home afterwards; there were oranges, bright with waxy skins, nuts to roast in the cinders, and sweets. He was so happy he felt sure he'd burst.

Father Christmas arrived looking very much like the vicar. He carried a bulging sack and when they had sung their carols he ceremoniously opened up the bag and began to call out the names from the labels stuck to each parcel.

'You can open 'em now,' one boy said. He'd been there last time it happened and knew the procedure. 'You don't have to wait till Christmas day.'

With excited fingers they tore open the wrapping paper. Freddie stared. He had a double decker bus, red, shiny and new. He stroked the paint work almost reverently.

'Happy Christmas!' the man with the white beard said.

'Happy Christmas!' they all yelled. 'Happy Christmas!' They didn't care if he **was** the vicar dressed up, the whole thing felt magic anyhow.

School was over until January. They had three wonderful weeks in which to play. Of course there were more presents on Christmas Day and a great goose to eat with stuffing and thick gravy: Mam even poured brandy over the plum pudding and set fire to it. Freddie felt the whole world had gone beautifully mad.

And then the snow came. Freddie knew at once something had happened. The moment he opened his eyes he could tell - the room was different, lighter.

He climbed carefully over the mound in bed that was his Dad. He'd never questioned why his father slept with him, he only knew it was a good feeling when he put his arms around him and pulled him close, hugging him against the cold, making him feel special.

He squashed his nose against the window pane. Everywhere looked so different, as if a huge hand had been out all night scattering icing sugar over the trees and buildings. You could hardly see some of the houses. The animals in the fields stood out like black cut-out shapes and the few people, already up, looked different somehow in their coloured scarves and hats.

'Dad.' He tugged at his father's hand. 'Wake up, Dad.'

John Airey grunted and turned over. It was Sunday. He didn't have to get up yet.

'Oh, Dad! Wake up. It's snowed. Everywhere's white. It looks lovely.'

He wanted to share the surprise. He was half afraid it would all disappear again before his father had a chance to see it.

'Snowed you say?' John Airey sat up, rubbing at his stubbled chin. He stared at Freddie, seeing the excitement trembling there. Then he sighed. 'I suppose it can't wait?'

'No. The lads'll be out there soon.' He left his father and ran back to the window. 'Can we go sledging? Can I have a sledge? Oh there's the Smiths! They're dragging a piece of corrugated iron tied with string - an' there's Roy Clarkson. He's come over from Towneley with his sledge.'

John Airey swung his legs over the edge of the bed stubbing his toes on the china pot they used in the night. Cursing softly he stood up.

At the window he put his arm round Freddie's shoulders. It was truly beautiful. No one could doubt God on a morning like this.

'Well,' he said. 'You're not goin' down Knob Stick Hill on a piece of metal sheeting that's for sure. If you come off you might cut yourself badly. You could end up loosing a leg or eye or somethin'.'

'Oh, Dad!' Freddie's face crumbled. He so desperately wanted to go out there with the others.

Slowly, his father smiled. 'I think we can do better than that,' he said.

'What do you mean?' Freddie was struggling into his flannel vest, pulling over his head the shirt made from an old one of his Dad's. He thrust his legs into a pair of

34

trousers. All the time his eyes were on his father.

Downstairs John Airey pushed him on to a chair. 'You're not goin' out till you've eaten,' he said. 'An' don't tell me you're not hungry 'cause you will be five minutes after gettin' out there in this weather.'

He pulled the cereal packet from a shelf. 'Here, you fill the dishes while I warm a pan of milk.'

Freddie did as he was told, pouring Force liberally into the blue and white enamel bowls, wishing his Dad wasn't always quite so sensible. He didn't mind using a bit of old iron for a sledge. All the other kids would be out before him. He wondered if Rita Clegg would call for him or just go straight on up with the rest.

Never in his life had he eaten breakfast so quickly. He was hopping up and down at the door hampering progress while his father tried to pull his arms through the sleeves of his jacket and tie a woollen hat over his ears.

'Aw, Dad! I look like a right cissy,' he protested.

'You'll be glad of it when the wind begins to bite.'

But they didn't make straight for Knob Stick Hill. First they went into the shed where his Dad made things.

His father pointed to the work bench. 'Know what that is?' he asked.

Freddie shook his head.

'Well, you will in a minute. I've just to put the runners on it and it's yours.'

Freddie felt as if his eyes would pop right out of his head. A real sledge. His Dad was making him a **real** sledge.

Oh the pride he felt as he pulled it over the snow. It glided like a bird. Freddie had never experienced anything like it in his whole life.

He waved to his Dad and then began the long climb to the top of the hill. The other children jostled for first place. Some had already been down and were on their way up again, others even now were whizzing past yelling with a mixture of glee and trepidation.

Freddie hauled his sledge up the last few yards to the top. It suddenly looked an awfully long way down. To the left of the track the ground dropped away steeply. He closed his eyes for a minute, trying to wipe out the picture of himself hurtling out over the edge, falling and falling.

'Get a move on, Freddie.' Someone behind him was urging him forward.

He sat down on the wooden slats. A boy gave him a push and he was off, hurtling down over the hard packed snow. Way ahead of him at the bottom he could see the river. It looked black and threatening. Suppose he couldn't stop? Suppose he went straight on down into the water?

The sledge slowed; with a thankful cry he leapt off pulling it to a standstill. He felt terrific. His sledge was faster than anything anyone else had. He felt like a king.

Laughing and talking excitedly he began the long trek back up to the top of the hill.

As the morning sped by he gained confidence. He didn't like the idea of the steep drop on the left, but if he just kept looking straight ahead and concentrated on the track in front of him he found he could almost ignore it altogether.

When he tried to think about it afterwards, he could never quite work out how the accident happened. One moment he was sliding down the hill - he remembered one of the boys yelling something to him and must have turned his head for a moment to see what it was all about - the next he was neck deep in icy cold water. The sledge had been built too well, gaining momentum with each new run as the track became smoother and smoother he had over-shot the end and was in the river.

He didn't know which frightened him the most, the thought of drowning or the thought of what his Mam would do when she saw the mess he was in.

A couple of adults had seen him enter the water; strong hands were pulling him out, voices admonishing him for being so stupid, so careless.

Suddenly he became mad. They were talking as if he'd done it on purpose! Did they think he **liked** plunging into freezing cold water?

'You'd better go straight home and change,' the man said. 'God help you if your Mam sees you like that.'

Freddie looked at the man in disgust. He didn't need anyone to tell him what his Mam was like.

Quietly he crept in through the back door. He couldn't hear her. She might be out the front or round at the pub, she was there more and more often these days.

Hurriedly he pulled off his wet clothes. Dry footed now he smuggled them upstairs, hiding them under the bed. His Dad would understand, he'd tell him tonight when there was no risk of his Mam finding out.

But he had to get back out. Someone else for sure would have rescued his sledge and be using it. Still shivering slightly he rejoined the boys and girls on the slope.

Dusk came early to the village of Cliviger. Suddenly the street lamps came on; golden light illuminated the sledging track in both directions turning it into a wonderful fairytale place.

A gasp rose in the air from the children. Freddie stopped to stare - it was so beautiful. Perhaps he **was** a little different to the rest, for the sight of it brought a lump to his throat and for a moment tears pricked his eyes.

He brushed his sodden sleeve across his face, pushing those thoughts to the back of his mind.

'I'll race you down,' he yelled to the boy next to him. 'An' if I win you owe me three glass alleys.'

Of course he knew he would win, a bit of him felt it wasn't fair to take advantage, another bit told him the scales wouldn't always be weighed in his favour and he'd best enjoy the golden moments when he had the chance. He could almost see those marbles being dropped into his hand.

Unnoticed, winter gave way to spring; it came to Cliviger in all its soft greenery, pushing away the biting winds, the shivery icy days when the horses slipped and slid about on the cobbles and red noses seemed to be the only part of some folks faces to appear from one week to the next.

Despite the warning, 'ner cast a clout till May be out', Freddie's Mam told him one morning that he could go outside without his overcoat on.

It felt like being let out of prison. He ran down the road, arms flapping. There was so much to investigate. He knew where to look for the thrush's eggs and where he'd find the first tender leaves of the dandelion they ate sometimes for dinner.

He was crouched down watching a toad laboriously making its way to the pond when he heard someone call his name. It was Lissie Carr, big Lizzie from Overtown, dressed in a fresh cotton dress without even a cardigan on. He watched her as she approached.

'What you doin'?'

He wasn't going to tell her, but then she smiled and he remembered the sweets - especially the toffees she sometimes gave to him - so he said, 'toads need water to keep their spawn in till it hatches. I was just goin' to follow this one and see it happen.'

She laughed, ruffling his hair. 'Aw, go on, you can see that another time. Come a walk with me.'

He stared at her, she must be sixteen and she was asking **him** to go a walk. Well, why not? It might prove interesting.

'You're not like the rest,' she said, swinging her hands alongside her skirt, looking down at him. 'Why are you different, Freddie? You always seem to be by yerself.'

'I'm adopted. It makes me different. But I'm **not** always by meself. I just like it sometimes.' He hopped from the shadows into the sunlight, feeling the warmth wrapping itself around his shoulders, and then...as he hopped back again it was as if someone snatched it suddenly away and the dark coolness settled once more upon him.

'You can come home with me if you like,' Lizzie said. 'Me Mam works day times an' me Dad's down the pit.'

'I can't come today. Not without tellin' someone where I've gone.' He had a vision of his Mam laying in to him with the strap.

She shrugged. 'Have it your own way, I don't care. But I'll give you some toffees when you do come. A whole bag full.'

'I will come. Next time,' he promised. He didn't want to miss an opportunity like that.

'Oh well...' Unexpectedly she stopped, almost tripping Freddie up with the suddenness of it. But she wasn't taking any notice of him. The head of one of the farm workers had appeared over the wall and he was grinning at Lizzie.

'Hello, Sydney Cartwright. What do you want?' she asked, but her voice was funny, kind of soft and enticing.

'You.' The man leered at her.

'Fancy that!' She tossed her head. 'What makes you think I want you?'

'I'll make it worth your while.'

She looked down at Freddie. 'I've got him with me.'

'Tell him to get lost for half an hour.'

Freddie was staring from one to the other. Something was going on that he didn't understand. He didn't much care for the feeling.

For a moment she seemed to hesitate, then she said, 'Oh, all right then.' She bent towards Freddie's face. 'Just go on, I'll give you some sweets next time I see you. Only you're not to tell anyone you've seen me...not with him.' She nodded at the head still peering over the wall like a Punch and Judy show.

Freddie felt disappointed but he knew it was useless to argue. He watched as she brazenly hitched up her skirts and disappeared over the wall. He could picture her falling in a heap on the grass with the labourer from the farm, but there his imagination deserted him.

Turning around he made his way back. Maybe the toad would still be there.

He had almost forgotten about the incident when next he saw her. She called out to him as if they were old friends. He waited for her to catch up with him.

'You got any sweets for me?' He hadn't forgotten that.

With shining blue eyes Lizzie smiled at him. 'Back home I 'ave. Do you want to come with me?'

He thought quickly. His Mam had gone shopping in town and wouldn't be back for hours and his Dad, he knew, was working until six o'clock. He nodded, wondering what sort of a house she lived in and why she didn't go to work like the other big girls did after they left school.

When he arrived he would have liked to look around, to poke about a bit, it wasn't very often he got invited into other people's houses - not unless they were relatives or had something to do with the chapel.

'Come on.' She looked excited. 'I'll show you my room.'

He followed her up the winding staircase. The room was long and narrow and the window so small little light filtered through. The bed looked lumpy, a faded flowery eiderdown trailed across the wooden floor boards.

'I'm goin to bed,' she announced.

He gazed at her in amazement. 'Now? What for?'

''Cause I want to. It's fun. Come on.'

She was already pulling off her frock. For a moment he caught a glimpse of her in her underwear, then she slipped between the sheets.

'Come on,' she urged. 'I'll give you sweets after.'

He wondered if he was supposed to undress. At home he wouldn't dare to get into bed with his outdoor clothes on. He bent down and took off his boots.

'And your trousers.' She giggled. 'You don't wear your trousers in bed do you?'

Afterwards, when he tried to think about it, he realised he hadn't been exactly scared, but he did have the uncomfortable feeling that what they did was somehow degrading. He didn't then have a word for it...he just felt like he ought not to be there, letting her run her hands over him like that...but she had promised him sweets.

She was gentle and kept telling him how nice he was. Once she took his hands and placed them on her chest. He could feel the softness of her breasts and the little lumps in the middle - but it was the things she was doing to him that were so curious.

He kept thinking about the toffees and wondering how long this had to go on before he could respectfully leave, having somehow earned the treat she'd promised him.

A sudden sound outside made her leap up. 'Oh God! I think it's me Mam. Get dressed,' she hissed. 'Quick!'

He was glad to, he didn't want to stay anyway. She was half dressed before he'd even got his trousers on.

'Take your boots.' She shoved them into his hand. 'You can put 'em on outside.'

'What about me sweets?' he demanded. He wasn't going without them.

'Here.' She thrust a bag into his hands. 'Now remember you don't say a word about comin' 'ere. This is our secret.'

But downstairs there wasn't anyone. She collapsed into a heap on one of the chairs. 'It must 'ave been the cat rummaging in the dustbin,' she told him.

'Can I still go?'

'Yes, you'd better. You can come again though. Did you like it?'

'It was alright,' Freddie conceded, peering into the paper bag. They were his favourite toffees. 'Okay, I'll come again some time.'

He ran off down the road. It was a tidy distance back and he'd best be home by the time his Mam got in. He hoped she'd be in a good mood. He hoped she wouldn't be smelling of beer, he hated that sickly sweet smell - no wonder his Dad never kissed her.

The day was fast approaching when egg rolling would take place at Thieveleys. All the people from Lancashire were coming, so someone told him.

'The eggs are boiled weeks before then seeped in a jar of vinegar to make them real hard,' his father explained. 'Then they paint them pretty colours and roll them down the hills. It's a sort of race. An Easter ritual to some folk.'

'Can we do it?' Freddie asked, liking the idea of painting the eggs most of all.

'No, we only watch. It's not for us.'

'Why, Dad? Why can't we do it?'

His father slipped an arm round his shoulders. 'It's just somethin' we don't do, son. But you'll enjoy watching the races just as much.'

Christine Sunter knew all about it, she lived at Thieveleys Farm. 'They come 'cause it's considered a beauty spot,' she explained. 'That's why folk come from all around. They do it on Easter Monday. We'll already have had our Easter eggs, we get them on the Sunday. Sometimes in church the children are given one after Sunday School,' she told him.

Freddie wished for a moment he was Church and not Chapel. Then Christine said, 'there's **something** we **can** do.'

'What's that?' Freddie was feeling slightly fed-up. He still didn't see why they couldn't have eggs of their own to roll.

'If we hide behind the hedge where the eggs roll so fast they can't keep up with them...'

'What? What can we do?'

She smiled at him, her brown eyes sparkling. 'You can help yourself to one if you're quick.'

'That's stealin'.' He looked at her waiting for her reaction.

'All the local children do it. It's part of the fun - us outwitting all the rest of the folk from Lancashire. It's...it's a kind of joke.'

They waited quietly, trying to suppress their excitement; peering through the bushes they observed the people arriving, setting up their picnics on tables under the trees.

A man in a black homburg hat seemed to be in charge of the proceedings. They heard his voice drifting across the lane.

'I will call one, two, three, then you place your eggs on the ground and begin to roll them.'

Christine, Freddie and three other children spread out, bodies tense, legs braced.

'I'll tell you when,' Christine said. 'You have to time it just right.'

With mounting excitement they waited; it was the daring - actually pinching the eggs from beneath their noses that made it feel so fantastic.

'Now!' She gave Freddie a sudden push.

He leapt out, body bent double as he scooped up a purple painted egg with his fingers. Panting with the effort he pushed his way back into the undergrowth. The others were looking at him. They each had a brightly coloured egg held firmly in their hands. They grinned triumphantly at each other.

'We'll get some more. Keep lookin',' Ronnie said.

They pocketed their gains and waited. The next run was just about to begin. They could hear some people searching fruitlessly on the other side of the hedge. Smothering their laughter they listened.

'I know mine's somewhere here. It must be in the grass.'

'They can't just disappear.'

'There were some children playing, do you suppose they saw them?'

Christine and her gang moved on, placing themselves strategically further down the field.

When it was the children's race they doubled their efforts. The children ran faster than the adults so that it became even more of a challenge to outwit them...them

41

foreigners.

When the visitors stopped chasing after eggs they set about the food. It looked like a banquet to the children of Cliviger. Hopefully they hung around. There was no harm in **looking** hungry.

'Here,' a man called out to them. 'We'll never eat all this lot, come and help yourselves.'

They needed no second bidding. There were things they had never tasted before - ham and salad sandwiches, rich fruit loaf, tiny cakes coated in chocolate and coconut. They ate until Ronnie was sick.

'Enough's enough,' said the man who had invited them. He wasn't smiling anymore - Ronnie had succeed in vomiting over his hat. 'Scram off now.'

They didn't mind, they couldn't have eaten another thing anyhow. In retrospect, the Egg Rolling Day they agreed had been quite a success.

Old Station Lane, Holme, down which hundreds of people walked to reach Thieveleys' where the egg-rolling took place

'What's next?' Freddie wanted to know. 'What happens next?'

It was a while before anyone cottoned on to what he was talking about.

'Well,' his Dad said, 'There's Whitsun and then the summer holidays. You'll be goin' over to Low Bradley then. You love it there, don't you?'

Freddie saw his Mam and Dad exchange looks. It seemed like his Dad was daring his Mam to contradict, but she only turned away, picking up a sock and starting to darn a hole the size of a potato in it; his Mam wasn't very good at sewing, to his mind it was because she kept her finger nails much too long but he dared not tell her.

'Yes, Dad.' he replied. 'We always have fun there on the farm and at Uncle Ted's. I wish you could come too.'

His Dad came him a gentle smile. 'Someone has to earn a living, son.'

Then there was the annual Walking Day jointly organized by the Todmorden Co-op and the Chapel. Every able-bodied man, woman and child from the village participated in this long walk.

Everyone was so happy, laughing and joking. The children ran ahead, a dancing ripple of colour against the green hedgerow. The girls stopped to pick flowers, running to hand them over to their mothers who would truly have preferred to complete the walk empty handed but dared not refuse the wilting bouquets.

Afterwards there was a party. Most of the adults made their way into the pub declaring they now deserved some liquid refreshment. Outside the children sat or lay on the grass warmed by the sun, drinking bottles of Tizer or Stone's ginger beer and talking about how they could earn money that summer.

'You have to think of somethin' people really want to buy,' Isobel said.

'Or something that's cheaper than they can get it anywhere else,' Smithy put in.

Freddie remained quiet, thinking. He was discovering he had quite a gift for painting. Suppose he could get hold of some paper doilies and paint them really pretty.

He pulled Rita to one side whispering in her ear. He knew if the others heard they might pinch his idea.

'My nan uses them,' she said. 'I could get some, I'm sure.'

'Then we could take them round to people's houses and tell them there's going to be a raffle and them's the prize,' Freddie announced, seeing himself suddenly with pockets full of money.

'How much would you charge?' Rita asked.

'Tuppence for five. It's better if you offer five. Me Dad told me people like to think they're gettin' a lot for their money. You'll have to write out the raffle tickets while I do the doilies.'

'Oh, that's not fair! Writing out all them tickets isn't fun.'

'Well, if you do 'em quick you can help me paint afterwards.'

It took a few days before they were ready. Clutching the brightly coloured paper doilies to their chests they knocked on the first door.

The woman stared at them. 'You must be mad,' she snapped. 'What would I want with doilies?' She slammed the door.

'She's not the right sort,' Freddie observed with an inborn wisdom. 'It has to be houses where people use doilies.'

They knocked and asked for most of the day. The response was disappointing to say the least, although one lady gave them a piece of ginger bread and Annie Schofield surprised them by giving them a penny each and telling them to keep the tickets. Perhaps she thought that way they'd leave her alone.

'I don't think it's such a good idea,' Rita decided. 'I'm goin home.'

Freddie looked at her in dismay. 'You can't give up yet.'

'I can.' She ran off scattering the tickets in the road in an untidy line.

He sighed. Girls weren't very good in business anyway. He'd have to think of something else tomorrow.

But the next day was Sunday, and Freddie knew, much as his Dad loved him, he'd never allow him to go round selling anything on a Sunday.

'I think you'll have to go without me to chapel this morning, son.' John Airey sat at the table looking right poorly.

'What's up, Dad?' Freddie was concerned, his Dad never missed chapel.

'Somethin's upset me - or your mam's cookin' is killin' me.'

Grace Mary looked at her husband. 'It's religion turnin' you sour. You don't know how to enjoy yerself anymore,' she said.

'Well boozin' yourself to death isn't my idea of enjoyment.'

'And just WHAT do you mean by that?'

Freddie crept away. It wasn't often his father could be goaded into an argument in front of him. He must really be feeling bad today.

He got himself ready for chapel. He'd go anyway. He knew it would please his Dad.

On the way he met up with the other children, some making their way to church, others to chapel. The clocks had been put forward and it felt strange, they tried to understand it and then gave up.

It wasn't until later when the service was over and they saw Annie Schofield all dressed up in her Sunday-best hurrying to church that they grasped what it was all about.

'She's forgot to change her clock,' one of them whispered.

'She's too late, the service is over.' Somebody giggled.

'Should we tell her?'

'No. Come on, let's follow her.'

They watched at a safe distance as she approached the church door. She tried the knob and then rattled it furiously. Slowly she turned about, noticing for the first time the group of round-eyed watching children.

'Is something wrong with the vicar do you know?' she asked.

'No, miss. But there's something wrong with you,' shouted one of the braver ones. 'You forgot to change your clock.'

And with one accord they all began to chant: Hickory dickory dock, she forgot to change her clock.....

Then, as if she had the power to turn them all into frogs, they turned and fled.

There was great excitement amongst the children from Holme School for Miss Handy had announced that morning there was to be a competition. Every child had to draw a map of the village and a special prize would be awarded to the child whose picture, judged by Miss Lancaster and the vicar, was considered to be the best.

'I'm going to use crayons,' Isobel Fawcett said. She had recently received a box for her birthday and was convinced that the more colour she put into her picture the more likely it was to win.

'What about you, Freddie?' Isobel asked. 'What will you do?'

'I'm thinkin' about it first. An' I don't think you should tell people anyway or they might pinch your idea.'

'But everyone's goin' to do the same picture.' Isobel looked at him puzzled. 'It's got to be a picture of the village.'

'I know that!' Fred said. 'But I'm still goin' to think about it first.'

Frowning after him, Isobel watched him wander away. She knew exactly how **she** was going to do **her** picture. She was going to stand at the end of the main street and draw the long row of houses and the pit with its big black wheel at the end.

Freddie had other ideas. If you wanted to make a map of the whole village then it stood to reason you had to get up high so that you could look down on it. He went to fetch his pencils and pad of paper that Miss Handy had given him last Christmas.

The village grew smaller and smaller as he climbed up over the fields. Grass hoppers and bees danced around his bare legs. He thought for a moment about the dragon flies who hovered over the pond - but that was now far below him and, regrettably, would have to be left out of his drawing.

For a long time he sat on the crest of the hill gazing down into the valley, his eyes storing away images of the village. It looked like a model one from where he sat - if he had been a giant he could have reached down and picked up the whole row of houses in one hand.

Thoughtfully he opened the pad and began to draw. Naturally, without any formal instruction, he knew how to fit the whole scene into the picture - nothing was cramped or left out; there was the row of houses, the mill, the tall chimney pots and the pit head, and beyond, reaching gently up to the horizon fields neatly contained by the darker green of the hedgerows.

Deeply concentrating, his brow wrinkled, Freddie licked at the lead tip of his pencil with a pink tongue.

It wasn't until his Dad sat down with a sigh beside him that he discovered how long he had been there.

'Your Mam was wondering what had happened to you. Supper's been ready this past hour.' His Dad leaned over inspecting the drawing. 'Did you do all that by yourself?'

'Yes.' Freddie dragged his eyes away and looked at his father. 'Is it alright, Dad?'

'It's perfect,' he assured him. 'If I'd never seen Cliviger before I'd recognise it from this. Don't change a thing.'

A beam of happiness shone from Freddie's eyes. 'Aw Dad! Really?'

'Did I ever lie to you son?'

His Dad stood up. 'But we'd best be gettin' back. You'll not want your Mam throwin' all your good work on the fire 'cause you're late, now will you?'

Freddie leapt to his feet. He knew this was no idle threat. Carefully he closed the pad.

Later that night, sitting in the window, using the last of the daylight, he put the finishing touches to his picture. He knew the sort of thing the rest of the children would do - he only hoped Miss Lancaster and the vicar liked his best.

There were three agonising long days to wait until the pictures were judged. For once there was no rustling or whispering as Miss Lancaster walked into the room with the vicar to make the announcement.

The children stood briskly to attention and chanted: 'Good morning, miss. Good morning, sir.'

Miss Handy was smiling as she stood to one side in order to make room for them. Freddie had the feeling she already knew who had won.

'All the entries were very good,' Miss Lancaster said. 'I am surprised how well you can now all draw. But one was exceptional. The vicar and I both agree that first prize goes to...' The children leaned forward, afraid they might miss their own name being called out. 'Yes, the first prize goes to Frederick Brayshay. Come up to the front,' she said.

He stumbled out from between the fixed seat and desk top, his face red with pleasure.

'Did you really do all of this picture yourself?' the vicar asked.

'Yes, sir.'

'Well...well I am impressed.' He handed over a postal order to Freddie. 'This will help you to buy some drawing materials. Keep it up, my boy. Who knows, we may have a famous artist in the village one day.'

Even his Mam was proud of him; for days after he kept over-hearing her telling the neighbours how he'd won the first prize and what the vicar had said.

When he went into town with his Dad they celebrated by going into a café and having tea and cakes. Then his father took him into the shop where they sold paints, and crayons, and painting books. It was hard trying to decide what to spend his money on but his Dad, with infinite patience, stood quietly by giving advice when asked, otherwise letting him make his own decisions.

One more unforgettable experience involving the whole village took place on May 6th 1935 - it was the silver jubilee of King George the Fifth and Queen Mary. The whole day was declared a national holiday.

In the streets of London the crowds were said to have surprised the royal couple - they were the biggest seen since the Armistice Day of 1918.

Over Cliviger hot air paper balloons filled the skies. They were inflated by flames from methylated spirits; a sight never before seen by the people of the village. In a field between Walk Mill and Overtown the children watched open-mouthed.

Then there were races to be run, endless mounds of food to be eaten, the judging of the best flowers and vegetables, and to top it all the presentation of a jubilee mug to each child.

Freddie clutched his tightly to his chest fearing he might drop it. There was a picture of the King and Queen Mary painted on the side. It seemed odd to be given presents when it was the King's celebration party. They really ought to have been giving presents to Him, he thought.

Soon after, news began to filter through from London that the King was ill; that the King wasn't going to survive. Who would succeed him? The obvious answer, everyone agreed, was Edward Prince of Wales. He would become Edward VIII. But unsettling nasty rumours were going around. He was seen too often with a Mrs Simpson. The ordinary folk had no time for her. They feared her influence over this weak man. Stories, exaggerated with the telling, began to spread like wildfire.

The children in their own way were influenced by the rumours. Before long they had created a song and could be heard chanting it all over the village for everyone to hear:

Who's that walkin down the street

Mrs Simpson sweaty feet

She's bin married twice before

An' now she's knockin at Edward's door.

Fashions, for no apparent reason, have their own way of appearing and disappearing. Other words, set to popular songs of the day, became a pastime for the children. 'Red Sails in the Sunset' was no exception. When they tired of Mrs Simpson they turned to Dr Buck Ruxton, recently convicted of murdering his wife. The thought of him being hung meant little to the children, the fun for them was in the song. Taking the tune they quickly invented words to sing to it:

Blood stains on the carpet

Blood stains on the knife

Oh Doctor Buck Ruxton

You've murdered your wife.

The Rag-n-Bone man was coming. 'Quick, quick,' the children shouted. 'You'll miss him.'

Everyone rushed indoors pleading for old rags. Anything would do. If it was made of wool all the better.

Freddie's Dad often brought home a bundle of cotton waste which he used for cleaning bits and pieces in his shed. Freddie tore open the shed door; frantically he began pushing around the things inside. He saw an old blue cardigan but no cotton waste. Only for a moment did he hesitate, this was surely enough to get him a gold-fish. He had wanted one for ages and ages.

The man, sitting on his cart, was inconceivably dirty; the grime on his skin made him appear almost black. His fingers protruded from the ends of his ragged gloves.

As he grinned encouragement to the children he revealed two brown stained teeth jutting up from his lower gums like miniature keeling grave stones.

Crowding around the cart they watched him, fascinated.

'What'cha got?' he asked Freddie.

On tip-toe Freddie reached up offering the blue cardigan.

The man handled it with the touch of a connoisseur. Hopefully Freddie waited for his verdict.

Through mouldy spikes of hair the man scratched at his skull. 'This yours?' he asked.

Well, it was - sort of. 'It's me Mam's but she don't want it no more. Can I have a goldfish, mister?'

'You'd better fetch a jam jar. An' put some water in it first.'

Freddie's feet barely touched the ground as he ran to the shed. He stood up on a box and pulled down a glass jar. In the kitchen he turned on the tap. He could hear his Mam out the back talking to someone. Before she could stop him, he rushed back to the Rag-n-Bone man.

''Ere you are then.' The gravelly voice addressed Freddie.

In his hands he held the jar, watching, fascinated by the beautiful orange fish swimming round and round. 'I'll call you Jimmy,' he said. 'I'll keep you forever.'

His Mam eyed the fish suspiciously. 'Where did you get that?'

'The Rag-n-Bone man gave it to me.' Freddie met her eyes defiantly. He'd never had a pet of his own before and he hoped most desperately that she'd let him keep it.

'He ought to 'ave more sense.' She turned away. 'You'll 'ave to feed it an clean it out yerself.'

'Oh, I will, Mam. I promise.'

It was several days before she missed her cardigan. Freddie was made to search in every corner of every cupboard and drawer.

'I can't find it, Mam,' he said, trying to look sufficiently concerned.

'Keep searchin', she instructed him. 'It can't 'ave run away.'

Freddie looked at his fish and smiled. He wasn't going to tell, and he was absolutely certain Jimmy wouldn't.

Chapter 3

BEGINNING OF THE END

Some of the children were going down to the River Calder to swim. Tentatively Freddie approached his mother. 'Please, Mam, can I go?'

'You don't 'ave a swimmin' costume.'

He stared at her miserable and defeated.

She glared at him impatiently. 'Oh, don't look at me like that.'

'But everyone's goin'.' She never understood how important it was to do what the rest of the gang were doing. If you didn't join in you soon got left out of everything. They'd most likely say he was a spoil sport or scared.

She looked at him, wheels clicking inside her head. 'Stay there,' she ordered and went upstairs.

He heard her pulling open the chest of drawers on the landing as he scuffed at the rag mat beneath his feet.

Coming back down to the kitchen she held something out to him. 'Here. You can borrow this. But you're not to get it wet.'

He looked at the swimming costume. It was the colour of Colman's mustard. It was **her** swim suit and it was too big, he knew it, even before he tried it on.

He wanted to tell her it wouldn't do, that he couldn't be seen wearing a woman's swimming costume, but that meant not going in the Calder at all. Reluctantly he took it from her.

'Remember, you're not to get it wet.' She frowned at him looking as if she might change her mind at any minute.

She must have been barmy to think he could go into the water without getting it wet. He could only hope it dried again before he had to return home.

He put it on under his shorts and shirt. If he got into the water and then slid his trousers and shirt off perhaps nobody would notice it was his mother's.

The river was low. Earlier in the year, when it had been in full flow they had come to watch; then it had been a wild crazy thrashing fury of foam and bubbles; it had torn at the roots of the huge trees clinging with a desperation to the banks of clay and earth - now they hung exposed above the water line.

Gasping as the cold of the river slapped against them, the boys slipped into the water. To Freddie's enormous relief no one even noticed the yellow swimming costume, they were all much too busy investigating the spooky world of gnarled roots. When you squeezed between them it looked as if you were in a strange underwater cathedral. It smelled of damp earth and the familiar smell of the river after the mills had done with it.

They played for hours, creating their own games, hunting, hiding, building a magical world of their own.

It wasn't until they finally left the water and Freddie glanced down at himself that he saw not only was the swim suit very wet, it was covered in a green slime of mud and weed.

There was no way of escape. With dragging feet he made his way home, knowing he'd get a lathering. The unfairness of it turned his heart to lead. He was, after all, only six; how could anyone be expected to play in a woman's swim suit in the river without getting it wet?

'I don't want your excuses,' she screamed at him. 'I warned you. You can't say I didn't warn you.' Her face was red, distorted with anger.

She pulled the leather strap from the hook on the back of the kitchen door. 'Perhaps this'll teach you.'

He felt the burning of his flesh and dug his teeth deep into his lip. He knew from bitter experience that crying or pleading with her would have no effect. The only hope of escape would be if his Dad walked in. But his Dad did not come.

Beaten and bleeding he crawled between the sheets. He tried to think about the fun they'd had in the river. He'd do it all over again if he got the chance. He wasn't going to let a few lashes with the belt stop him he told himself with as much bravado as he could muster.

It wasn't until much later that night when his Dad crept into bed beside him and pulled him into his lap that he let out a cry of pain.

'What is it, Freddie?'

'I'm hurtin', Dad.'

'Why's that, son?'

'Me Mam belted me.'

He felt his father's body stiffen. 'Was it a bad hiding?' he asked quietly.

'Quite bad.'

'It can't go on. I've got to do somethin'.' He spoke almost to himself, all the while gently stroking Freddie's fair head. 'Don't worry, son. I'll see it doesn't happen again.'

Freddie closed his eyes. He was very tired. He knew his Dad meant well, but he was too gentle, he'd never be able to stop his Mam.

The long hot summer continued and with it came the desire to play again with the other children down on the banks of the Calder.

Freddie appealed once more to his mother: 'Can I have a swim suit of me own? Just trunks like the other lads? Please, Mam?'

He was seeing less and less of her these days, and although it was hard coming home from school having to wait around for what seemed like hours until she arrived to let him in, during the holidays it didn't matter.

She seemed distracted. He knew she and his Dad were talking about taking a pub and moving. He wasn't sure he cared one way or the other; it was over at Holme Chapel so he'd still go to the same school.

'You can borrow mine again,' she said, surprising him. 'There isn't any money for new clothes, we're goin' to need all we've got if we take the pub.'

It was the best he could hope for. Trying to look grateful he went in search of a piece of towel and found an old roller one that usually hung on the kitchen door - now too threadbare to serve even that purpose he wrapped it around the swim suit. He hoped she wouldn't complain when she found out.

Pulling on the swim suit he ran out of the house before she changed her mind or thought up some chore for him to do.

The river appeared different, usually so murky and yellow, today it looked brilliant with the sunlight dancing and sparkling on the water's surface. You could lie down on the bank, scoop it up into your hands and drink the clear water.

'There's monsters lurking down there,' one of the Smith boys said. 'We have to try and capture 'em.'

'What you goin' to use?' Freddie asked, venturing at once into the spirit of the game.

'I've made a noose of wire. You go on first and when you see a monster you drive it this way. I'll dangle the wire over this strip of water here and he'll come along an' get his head trapped in it.'

'How will I know what he looks like?' Freddie asked.

'You can't mistake a monster for anything else, it's long and green and looks like a...a crocodile.'

As neither of them had ever seen a live crocodile they had only their imaginations and a picture they'd seen in a school book to go on. It sounded like a fair description.

Thus informed, Freddie waded in between the roots of the trees; half-hidden by the water they gave the impression of something weird and fearful...lurking, waiting. It wasn't difficult to imagine they were alive, watching, ready to snap at his legs with hundreds of sharp white teeth.

He'd wait a while, he decided, let Smithy build up the scene with the other lads who were now arriving; perhaps he'd send someone down to help him. He stood quite still, breathing deeply. He could hear Smithy shouting instructions, detailing the other lads to block off the rest of the escape routes.

Suddenly a great swirl of warm water, discharged from the mill, came rushing towards him. Before he even had time to shout a warning to the others it knocked him off his feet burying his head for a several seconds beneath the filthy turbulent yellow foam. Spitting and spluttering he gained a foothold and yelled to Smithy.

There was an eerie silence and then he heard a disembodied voice call, 'I'm here.'

Freddie peered through the murky shadows. 'I can't see you,' he called back, picturing his voice winding its way through the roots, reaching out to his playmate.

Smithy's voice was raised in panic. 'I'm stuck. I got washed off me feet. Somehow I've got jammed. I...I can't move.'

Freddie inched nearer to the voice. 'Can't you move at all?' he asked.

'I just said I couldn't, didn't I?'

Then he saw him, his face a pale sickly colour just showing above the water. He looked strangely shortened.

'Where's your legs?' Freddie tried to see through the water but it was impossible.

'They're bent under me an' the roots of the tree's trappin' em.

If another surge of water comes I'll drown.' His voice was shrill, it didn't sound like Smithy at all anymore.

Freddie knew the mill was likely to discharge more water into the Calder, they always did this when they emptied the boilers about an hour before they closed up the place for the night: he'd been there many a time watching his Dad turning the great wheels and had personally witnessed the water, suddenly unleashed, thrusting itself like a great wall out into the daylight, swelling the Calder, rushing wildly past the banks of the river.

He realised with a sickening sense of fear his own inability to fight it. 'I'll go an' get help,' he said.

'Don't leave me.' Smithy was crying now. Freddie could hear him trying to hold back his sobs. 'I don't want to die.'

'That's why I 'ave to fetch help. I'll come back in a few minutes.'

Holding on to the branches with a fierce desperation Freddie pulled himself forward, out of the tree root cathedral that had changed into a horrific nightmare, a place of terror.

He grabbed hold of an outstretched hand and saw a naked body leaning over hauling him out of the water

'Smithy's trapped,' he gasped. 'Come on, we've got to get him out. He's goin' to drown if we don't hurry.'

Freddie looked round wildly. 'Has anyone got a knife?'

No one had. Between them they produced only sticks and string and a piece of wire.

Splashing loudly, dragging his feet through the swirling water, he lead them back.

Smithy was swearing now, not caring who heard him. 'Get me out. Bloody get me out of here.'

One of the older boys who could swim ducked down under the water. Feeling around amongst the roots and debris he located the twisted legs. A minute later he surfaced wiping the filthy water from his eyes. 'I think I can hold back the roots if someone can pull him loose,' he announced. He looked at Smithy whose eyes now appeared like dark smudges, as if someone had pushed their thumb into his face making splodgy holes.

'When you feel me move the roots kick with your legs an' shout,' he ordered. 'And when you hear him shout,' he told Freddie. 'Pull like hell.'

'I don't know if I can.' Smithy said. 'Suppose me legs are broken.'

'Do they feel broken?' Freddie asked. This was going from bad to worse. For a moment he thought about the yellow swim suit and knew his mother would half kill him when he got home.

'I can't feel me legs,' Smithy told them. 'They're sort of cold and numb.'

'Well', said the boy who could swim. 'You've got to try. Otherwise you'll jus' drown.'

Before Smithy could protest he took a great gulp of air and disappeared beneath the water's surface.

Freddie waited, his heart was thundering in his ears. It felt as if **he** was the one about to die.

'Aaah!' Smithy yelled and Freddie grabbed him under his arm pits and heaved.

'Kick,' he shouted. 'Kick!'

For a moment they both disappeared beneath the swirling murky foam, and then, coughing, choking, spluttering, they surfaced. Smithy was free.

On the bank they lay panting; for several minutes it was too painful to try and speak. Freddie looked at Smithy - his eyes were open and he gave him a sickly grin. The feeling of relief threatened to overwhelm him. 'Your legs all right?' Freddie asked.

Smithy nodded. 'I think so.' He screwed up his eyes and peered at them, observing with a kind of pride the scratches and bruises beginning to appear. 'We'd better not tell anyone what happened though or we'll get a hiding.'

Freddie sighed. He'd get one anyway. 'Perhaps we could just lie here till we're dry,' he suggested.

But one of the children had run home and reported that someone was drowning. A crowd had gathered. They stared down at the boys with curious probing eyes.

Smithy and Freddie sat up. 'It was just a game,' they said sheepishly.

But when he got home Freddie's mother didn't think so. 'A game?' she screamed. 'That does it, we either move from here or I'm leavin' you and yer father. I'm not puttin' up with anymore.'

He didn't take her too seriously. He didn't truly believe she meant it - that was until the day of his birthday when his Dad told him.

All that is left of the River Calder - a sad scene demonstrating the results from industry indiscriminately drawing water from the rivers

His father had made him a beautiful bow and arrow for his birthday. He was now eight years old and considered sensible enough to use it without damaging other people or their property.

It wasn't an ordinary bow, his Dad had made it from steel, and the arrows were dead straight with shiny metal tips.

They were standing together by the mill chimney looking up into the sky. Freddie clutched the bow in his hands. 'Do you reckon you could send an arrow up as high as the chimney?' his Dad asked.

Freddie stared, the chimney looked enormous. 'Could we, Dad?'

'Let's give it a try.'

They must have stood there for hours taking it in turns until Freddie's arms felt as if they were made of lead and a pain like a red hot wire ran up and down his back.

Finally his Dad said, 'Let's call it a day, I have to talk to you anyway.'

They sat down on a soft green hillock where they could watch the swallows gathering, ready to make their long journey to a place in the sun before the cold snows of winter returned.

'Freddie, I know you're a sensible lad and that you'd do anything to try to help me,' his Dad began.

'Yes, Dad.' Why did he feel suddenly so afraid?

'Well, your Mam and me...well, we've decided to move an' take The Queen Hotel over at Holme Chapel.'

'Oh, Dad!' He looked at his father in dismay. 'I thought you didn't like pubs. I thought that you didn't want to go.'

The big man sighed. 'That's true. But sometimes we have to do things we don't much want to do if we think they're best at the time. Your Mam's set her heart on it. We've got to give it a try for her sake.'

'I don't want to live in a pub.' Freddie recalled the noise, the smell, the people who drank too much. He'd even heard someone say once that Grace Mary danced on the table - everyone knew that meant his mother was a loose woman when she'd had too much to drink. It made him angry at the time - then, as he had realised the truth of it and that his Mam did sometimes drink more than she should, he had felt physically sick.

'You won't have to live there,' his father told him. 'Not much of the time anyhow. You can go over to your uncle at Bradley weekends and holidays, an' you've got the Clarksons. I've had a word with them, they've said they'll make you welcome any time.'

'Will I still see you, Dad?'

His father's arm pulled him close. 'Of course you will. I'll be at the pub all day and night helpin'. I'll not be goin' to the mill anymore.'

Freddie was amazed. He couldn't imagine it. For as long back as he could remember his Dad had been engineer at the mill.

He turned to look into his father's sad grey eyes. 'Won't you be an engineer anymore, Dad?'

'Course I will. You can't stop being what you already are. It jus' means I won't be using them skills for a time.'

'Oh!' There wasn't much else to say.

'I want you to help me, son. Be good to your Mam an' try not to cross her. It's a big undertakin'. We have to try an' make it work.'

'Alright, Dad.' He wanted to hug him, but he was eight now and he knew he was too big to go making a fuss where folk could see him. He wished he could say he loved him. He hoped his Dad understood.

That night, lying open-eyed in his bed, he began to recall many of the wondrous things his Dad had done for him and made for him during the time they had lived there in the Co-op Buildings.

There were those fantastic rides they had had together on his Dad's Sun motorbike - the only one in the whole village - sitting astride the metal rack with no pillion seat, bumping and bobbing along the lanes in what always seemed to be the middle of the night with his Dad close behind him, laughing. He pictured the carbide headlights flooding the whole valley, picking up the hills, turning them into strange animal shapes. The lights themselves were like magic, just a lump of carbide - his Dad had often shown him - producing gas that ignited when the damp got to it.

He gave a little laugh remembering the time he'd taken some and put it into a bottle, throwing it into the river; the explosion when it hit the water was like something out of one of the comics he read at the house in Bradley.

Then there was the hoop his Dad had made out of steel. All the kids had watched with envy as he drove it through the village. It had a handle with a small loop fixed to it so that as the metal hoop ran through it there was this lovely swishing noise. Swish. Swish. Swish.

He thought with regret that there would be no more times when he would go to the mill with his Dad, watching him as he let off the steam from the huge boilers. The noise was deafening; there were the big leather belts driving the shafts, slapping round and round...and there was his Dad oiling all the parts of the beam steam engine, proud and confident, in charge of everything and knowing how good he was at his job.

Freddie tried to imagine what it would be like never to see again all the things that made up his life here in Cliviger. Never again to watch the steam train on the horizon from his bedroom window as it chuffed and puffed its way up the hill, slipping and struggling all the way to the top. And then, out of the trucks thousands of white match-stick objects would fly into the air. It was a long time before he had discovered they were the pit props, used for supporting the roof of the pit, looking so tiny from such a long way off.

Suddenly a bad feeling slipped into his mind; his Dad had never made him a fairy cycle. Everybody else in the village seemed to have one but his Dad, even though he'd promised, had never made one for him. He supposed now he never would. He had long outgrown his tricycle; if he tried to ride it his knees hit the handle bars and he had given up after his teacher asked him where all the bruises had come from.

Fretfully he turned in his bed wishing his thoughts would stop, wishing he didn't have to go to Holme. He didn't want to leave behind all the things he loved; his friends, the adventures they shared playing together in the village.

Oh, he knew that some of the things they had done had been crazy, but such fun; the rolling of great slithers of slate down the hill must have been about the most dangerous thing they had ever done. He could see them now, those great pieces of grey slate rolling and bouncing their way down toward the road as they watched, holding their breath for fear they would actually reach the tarmac - maybe hitting a car or horse and cart, even a person. But they had never reached the road.

He buried his face in the pillow, yet still the pictures tormented him. Clear in his mind he saw the archway entrance to the pit right next to Long Row with its black iron railings, and men leading the ponies along the shafts to the coal face, and small trucks joined together with a continuous chain coming out loaded with jet black coal.

He wondered how those men, covered with coal dust that crept into every crease of their bodies, ever managed to wash it all away; but he knew they did, he'd watched them many a night practising their music, immaculately dressed in their uniforms with peaked caps and shining silver buttons, members of the Cliviger Prize Silver Band playing music that set your feet tapping. He could see all the faces of the older Smith brothers who played in the band, and an invisible constriction caught at his throat choking him.

Freddie felt the tears soaking his pillow, knowing he must hide his distress. He had promised his Dad to help, he must never let him find out how much he hated the idea of leaving. It felt as if his life was about to end.

There was still school to be got through the next day. He couldn't tell anyone. He had made up his mind for as long as he stayed in Cliviger he would carry on just the same, as if nothing was going to happen. He'd try to pretend his life wasn't about to fall apart. He wondered if he would ever be happy again.

That night as they left the school gates the children debated as usual whether to take the long way home. They had agreed long ago that the black scottie dog from Weston's was going to get one of them sooner or later. A deep rumbling growl would begin somewhere in its throat as they approached, rising gradually until it became a frenzied aggressive barking that went on and on. It made your blood run cold just to hear it and all the children were terrified of him. Walking the long way home meant avoiding the Weston's dog.

Freddie squared his shoulders. He didn't care any longer. 'I'm goin to walk straight past,' he announced. 'I'm not walkin' all the way round anymore.'

Isobel stared at him. 'He'll bite you,' she told him. 'You'll probably get lock jaw an' die.'

'I don't care,' Freddie said, really believing it. 'You lot don't have to come if you're scared.'

He lead the way, the rest of the gang trailing behind. It felt alright until he saw ahead of him the wall of the Weston's grounds; his steps slowed as he strained his ears listening for the dog. There was no sound. This was the moment when, if he was going to make it, he should take to his heels and run like mad, but if he did the others would think he was frightened after all and whatever happened he mustn't lose face.

His hands felt hot and clammy and his heart began to thump too loudly beneath his shirt. He was almost there. Freddie quickened his pace slightly - and then it happened: from nowhere the black hairy body of the dog hurtled through the opened gateway and rushed at Freddie's legs.

'Get down! Get off!' Freddie yelled reaching out with his boot. He was going to kick that dog to death if it touched him. But the dog had stopped, it looked up at Freddie, confused. Head-on confrontation was something it had never experienced before. Freddie stared back 'Go home,' he said sternly, trying to look two feet taller than he really was. 'Go home you bad dog!'

The group of children, standing some twenty yards off, let out a cry of amazement as the dog turned and ran back to his house.

Freddie looked over his shoulder and grinned. 'I told you,' he said. 'There's nothing to it. You just mustn't ever let them see you're afraid.'

He felt like a king with his courtiers following respectfully behind him as he completed his walk back to the village. If he had to leave Cliviger this was the time to go. None of them were ever going to forget that it was Freddie Brayshay who had finally dared to challenge the Weston's savage dog.

Chapter 4

LIFE AT HOLME CHAPEL

Soon after, they moved into The Queen Hotel. It seemed to Freddie that a time of upheaval had entered his life and there was no end to it. For weeks he had been staying with someone else, only seeing his Dad on odd occasions. His mother he barely saw at all. When he did, she would have a long cigarette holder drooping from her fingers with a Du Maurier cigarette stuck in it; her hair was set in curves around her face, and the face itself, looking strange and alien, was covered with the new make-up she'd taken to using since becoming a landlady.

Upstairs above the front of the building was an enormous room. Freddie never forgot the first time he discovered it. He'd heard his Dad speak of it as the Valuation Room. Inquisitive to discover what lay on the other side of the door, forbidden to enter, he waited his opportunity.

The day came: a charabanc of people had stopped outside the pub and as he listened to their unfamiliar voices he knew that for the next couple of hours his parents would have no time at all to wonder about him or what he was up to.

With a pending sense of excitement he climbed the stairs. The dark varnished door creaked stiffly on unused hinges. Freddie peered into the gloomy interior. It was crammed full of furniture of every shape and size. Three old pianos immediately captured his attention as he moved forward. His fingers plonked down on the keys sending the sound rolling around the room. It was like an Aladdin's cave.

He never told anyone of his discovery. This place was his. He could come here any time he chose. He knew from listening that the whole load of furniture had been forced upon his Mam and Dad when they bought the place; it filled the function room which should have been used for splendid banquets, wedding feasts and the like - instead, it became his own special place rarely, if ever, entered by another human being.

The cat had given birth to three kittens. Freddie looked at them in wonder, longing for the day when they would open their eyes, he thought it would be lovely watching them, playing with them, teaching them to catch mice.

John Airey had other ideas. 'Stop that cat!' he shouted. 'Don't let her get out of the room.'

He had never seen his Dad like this before. His eyes were wild as he rushed about leaping at the cat who, with equal determination was attempting to get back to her family.

Divided between wanting to help his father and save the kittens, Freddie hesitated.

'Jump to it!' His Dad was shouting louder than ever.

There was no way of avoiding what followed. Filling a 36 gallon barrel with water he ordered Freddie to hold open the lid. He watched, appalled, horrified, as his father dropped the tiny bodies into the water. Without a word he slammed shut the lid leaving the kittens to drown. Freddie stepped back. He felt bewildered and sickened. This wasn't **his** Dad. **His** Dad would never do anything so cruel. He couldn't even begin to make sense of what was happening. His mind was haunted by the thought of those tiny kittens drowning, he imagined he could hear their pitiful mewing.

'That's that then,' his Dad said. 'It had to happen.'

Silently, head bowed with shame, Freddie turned away. Climbing the stairs he hid himself in the Valuation Room. Something awful was happening to his Dad and he didn't know how to stop it.

But then there were those glorious times when he escaped from it all, sitting at Uncle Ted's kitchen table, drawing and painting. His pictures were getting to look really quite nice. He wished he could sell them. He wished he could make so much money his Dad could leave the pub. Though he never spoke of it he knew he hated it. He knew the minister at the chapel thought it was a bad thing too.

Powerless to halt the progress of events he watched his Dad growing more and more miserable. He no longer made him things and when they were together a dark shadow seemed to settle on them.

His Dad was also getting thinner and thinner, even his hair had started to look thin. He wondered if his Mam had stopped cooking dinners for him. Freddie got a dinner now at school - or rather the house right next to The Queen at Mrs Allenby's. All the children traipsed round there from school every day at half past twelve. The dinners were splendid, whopping great tins of steak and kidney pudding or beef stew; there was always pudding afterwards too, spotted dick, treacle tart and custard, jam roly poly. His body began to fill out, he could almost feel himself growing stronger and when he bent his arm now and clenched his fist he could show off the muscles appearing in his upper arm.

Abruptly, one day, it all came to an end. The children were told that they would not be going to Mrs Allenby's anymore. Miss Lancaster made the announcement in a voice that forbade any questioning.

It was only after school, listening to the groups of whispering women at the street corners that the children discovered the truth.

'She was found drowned in the pond,' one of the women said. 'In Macnamara's grounds.'

'Never!' Another women gasped a response. 'What was she doin' there?'

'No one knows. They say she did herself in.'

'That's a sin against God!' There was a shocked silence as the women, realising the significance of this, stared at each other in trepidation tinged with excitement.

The children strained to hear more. What had happened to Mrs Allenby? What would God do?

'They'll not let her be buried in the churchyard,' the first woman said. She seemed to know everything. 'They'll bury her at the cross roads to keep the devil away.'

Turning suddenly she caught sight of the children. 'You push off,' she told them. 'It's nothin' to do with you.'

But of course it was. They wouldn't be getting anymore hot dinners. Freddie wished he'd remembered to thank her more often. Now it was too late. It must be a terrible thing to kill yourself.

The Queen Hotel as it is today. The house immediately to the right was the home of Mrs Allenby.

Competition between their pub and the other one in the village was fierce and causing concern for his parents. Perhaps, Freddie thought, if his Mam had stopped drinking so much they might have made it, the customers seemed to like her. But reason told him it was more to do with his Dad hating all of it - the booze, the drunks, the coarse jokes - he couldn't wait to throw the customers out each night when the clock struck ten.

Nellie Crowther came to work at the pub. Freddie hated her. He often heard the whisperings that went on between his Mam and this awful woman. He hid, spying on her, sure that one day he'd catch her stealing money from the till. Her eyes, green with strange yellow rings around the pupils, had a way of watching him without her head turning; cold eyes that followed him, almost as if she knew what he was thinking.

She seemed to spend hours on her doorstep when she wasn't helping in the pub; arms folded across her apron, staring up or down the road, just as if **she** was waiting to catch **him** out. He wished he could tell his Dad, but there wasn't anything definite to report, just those horrible feelings that wouldn't go away.

One day she called out to him. Freddie froze. She said his name again, this time her voice was soft and wheedling. 'Come on here,' she said.

Suspiciously he edged forward.

To his amazement she opened the door wide. 'Come on in a minute,' she said. 'I want to talk to you.'

Curiosity struggled with fear. He wanted to know what her house was like. He could almost imagine the rats and witch's cauldron bubbling on the fire. But suppose she caught him and put HIM in the pot.

She smiled, showing nicotine stained teeth. 'I'm not goin to bite you. Come on.'

He followed her into the front room. To his astonishment it was sparkling clean. China ornaments stood on the mantle piece and a big green plant was sitting in the hearth in front of the empty fire place. A white crocheted cloth was spread over the table and a bowl of shiny artificial fruit stood in the centre of it. His face brightened.

'Now, Freddie,' she was still using that funny voice. 'I know a pub isn't the best place for a lad like you to grow up in. I've talked to your Mam about it lots of times.'

'I'm not there much.' Freddie stared at her unblinking. 'I go over to Bradley holiday times an' I've got me friends, the Clarksons.'

'Still, it's not the best place to be. So, I was wonderin'...what about you comin' to live here with me?'

'Here?' He couldn't believe his ears.

'Aye. I'll be good to yer. You can have yer own room - that's if yer want it.'

Freddie began to back away. He didn't like what he was hearing. He didn't trust her, not one inch. 'Me Dad wouldn't let me,' he said.

'Oh, your Dad!' She laughed derisively. 'I don't think he has much say in things.' The green eyes glittered.

Now he was beginning to hate her. It felt better than being afraid. 'I'm not comin', he said. 'I don't want to.'

He turned, stumbling over the door step, out into the sunshine, out into the clean fresh air. He didn't stop running until he reached his own back door.

The effects of the slump began to bite. It didn't mean anything at first, not until the men and women who had worked all their lives at the mill and the pit began to moan about their time being cut and threatened redundancies.

'What's it all about, Dad?' he asked on one of those rare lovely days when he accompanied his father to chapel.

'No one quite knows how it started,' his Dad replied. 'There just isn't enough money to go round. People are buying less, factories are closing down, there's goin' to be more an' more people out of work.'

'But you've got a job,' he protested.

'Not if the customers don't drink I haven't.'

His Dad paused. 'Look, Freddie. I've got to do somethin' about you before it's too late. I know you'll try to be a good lad...so I've asked a friend of mine if you can go an' stay with her for a while.'

Freddie pricked up his ears. 'Who is she?'

'You're to call her auntie. She's a very good lady. She'll look after you.' He stopped. He still looked sad.

'What's the matter, Dad?'

'She lives in Long Row, that's all.'

'Long Row!' He stared at his Dad in open horror. 'But nobody goes to live there, not unless...not unless...' He didn't know how to express himself. He believed that was where all the poverty stricken people with no money at all ended up.

His father seemed not to notice his response. 'She's a nice lady, that's what really matters.' he said. 'An' I promise you she won't take a belt to you.'

He went, a feeling of shame reddening the tips of his ears. He wondered what his friends at school would say. He knew he looked a freak. He now wore his Dad's

64

trousers cut off at the knee, hastily hemmed by inexperienced fingers. Even his shirts were old ones of his Dad's with the frayed collars snipped off.

Slowly he learned that others were in the same predicament; it seemed everyone was on the downward slide to disaster. A strange new word entered their vocabulary. Slump.

Only in the school paddock where they played their own games did the terrible burden ever really seem to leave him these days.

During hours and hours of endless play they created a world of their own, playing buses and charabancs and cars, their feet and knees etching their own paths. Piles of bricks and stones became famous buildings; they made houses and factories; they created a perfect world where there was enough for everyone and games to satisfy the most adventurous. In the Paddock there was no Long Row and no pubs.

At the end of the day they would return home with voices so hoarse from hours of imitating the sounds of motors and engines that they could hardly speak.

Long Row, Cliviger, as it is today

The school children were busy rehearsing; there was to be a concert and everyone was taking part. Freddie felt a tingle of pride when he thought of his part: his class were going to sing a song and he, with four other boys, were to fire off their pop guns at the end of each verse. He never tired of rehearsing. He knew his Dad would be there too for he was going to be singing on stage later. Freddie was determined to make his Dad proud of him.

The concert was to run for five days. For the moment the recession and hardships were forgotten. From somewhere materials were found to make the costumes the children were to wear. Freddie looked down at himself feeling kind of funny in his hunter's clothes.

The great moment finally arrived. He was on stage standing in line at the front with the other boys each holding a pop-gun ready to fire.

The rest of the class began to sing:

Who's afraid of the big bad wolf,

Big bad wolf, big bad wolf,

Whose afraid of the big bad wolf...

The moment had come, as their words faded the boys in turn fired their guns: BANG. BANG. BANG. BANG...Bop.

Freddie felt his face turn scarlet. He'd done it again. Despite all the hours of rehearsal he'd missed the timing. He heard someone snigger. It was no use - at the end of each verse he knew now he'd get it wrong.

It had always been the same. He **was** different. He was adopted. He could never truly be one of the village, one of the family. Always he had been made to feel a bit of an outsider. Sometimes it had spurred him on to make greater effort, to show them all that he was **somebody**. He knew in the past that his father had given him more time than the other boy's dads, that he'd made him more toys than the rest, trying to compensate. But it hadn't worked. Nothing could change the reality of what he was. ADOPTED.

Suddenly he didn't care. He didn't care what anyone thought. One day he'd show them. He blinked back angry tears of frustration. He'd show them all.

Then it was over and his Dad was standing there on the empty stage. He looked splendid. Freddie knew he was going to sing his favourite song, The Cornish Floral Dance.

There was a lump in his throat as he watched and listened. It seemed he was seeing his father as he had never seen him before, remembering how he iused to be - tall, lean, with powerful shoulders from previous years of swimming, and his hair, like wind-swept grass smoothed down. But the most compelling thing was the fierceness in his steel grey eyes. They **made** you look. They **made** you listen.

This was **his** father, honest, caring, industrious, and Freddie knew, without being able to put it into words, that his Dad was incorruptible.

One day, quite unexpectedly, he discovered his parents had split up and left the pub. He had no idea what had happened to his Mam. His Dad he saw now only on rare occasions.

It was as he played one day near the lane that lead to the edge of the village that he saw, for the first time, his father as others saw him. A group of people were loitering there dressed in their Sunday-best when they spied his Dad returning from chapel.

'Hey look!' someone shouted. 'Here comes Moses'.

One man, bolder than the rest, called down to him. 'Hey there, Moses. Had any visions lately?'

Freddie stared. It was **his** Dad they were calling Moses. **His** Dad they were mocking. The bottom seemed to be falling out of his stomach. He wanted to turn and run away, to hide where no-one would ever find him. But his eyes were held by that familiar figure. He saw now how ill his father looked, so thin and poor. Why were they all being so cruel? Why did everyone laugh at him?

'It's 'cause he's become a Jehovah's Witness,' an older boy explained. 'He thinks the rest of the world is damned. If you don't repent and join them you'll go to hell.'

Shame washed over him as Freddie watched, silent, numb, unable to attack the mob who laughed and chaffed at his Dad. Bitterness struck deep into his heart. The man he loved, the only person he had ever loved was the laughing stock of the village.

He felt a searing hate for the woman who, he was convinced, had caused his father's downfall. Why couldn't his Mam have left them alone? Why did she have to go to that stinking pub anyway? His Dad had been tall and proud when he was engineer at the mill. Look what she'd done to him.

A few days later he came to take him away. He'd seen his father briefly and he'd tried to explain to him. 'We just don't have any money at all, son. We've lost everythin'. We're bankrupt. Auntie can't go on keepin' you. It's only for a while. Once I'm on me feet I'll fetch you.'

He didn't argue. They had said he had to go. They all said it. The whole village seemed to be shouting it in his ears. St George's Home For Waifs and Strays was where they were sending him.

Chapter 5

ST. GEORGE'S HOME FOR WAIFS AND STRAYS

Number Eight Vine Street, Kersal, Salford, Manchester. It was his new address. His new home where he would have no Mam or Dad and no-one knew him.

The door opened - they hadn't even rung the bell yet - it was just as if the people inside the building had been waiting for him.

A tall man wearing a smart suit and shiny black polished shoes bent down and spoke. 'Hello. I'm Mr Nicholson, your Headmaster.'

His Dad gave him a gentle shove. 'Go on, Freddie. Say, "hello, sir".'

He opened his mouth but no sound came.

The man took him by the shoulder. 'Cat got your tongue?' he said. 'Well, never mind. I expect you'll soon find it again after you get to know everybody.'

He was talking to his Dad now; Freddie looked around. This was his new home. It felt so strange. He was going to sleep here. He'd wake up each morning and he'd still be here. Staying in this place he'd never be able to go over to the Clarksons again or sit at Uncle Ted's table painting. He'd not see his school mates or be able to swim in the Calder. It was unreal. It was only a dream and soon he'd wake up and find himself.....

Somehow they had ushered him down the corridor and he found himself standing just inside the doorway of a playroom. They had been showing him around he realised, but the vast building with its many rooms had had no impact until this moment. Freddie stared, turning slowly, looking at the great room, seeing several children drawing on the walls.

Mr Nicholson followed the direction of his gaze. 'Oh, it's alright, they have permission. They're painting a mural. Do you like to paint, Brayshay?'

Freddie nodded, watching the children busy at their task, so neatly dressed in navy blue jumpers with red collars, grey shorts and socks, and black lace-up shoes. He became aware of the cleanliness, the sense of law and order. Each child wore a canvas apron over his clothes tied at the back with white tapes.

'Now say goodbye to your father.' That cold clipped voice was addressing him again.

He wanted to hug his Dad, to reassure him that he didn't mind being there. He could see how wretched he looked. But the man was watching them and he didn't want to shame his father. He was desperately afraid his Dad was going to cry.

'Cheerio, Dad.' He managed a bright cheerful voice. 'It's fine here. I'm goin' to like it.'

'Be a good lad, Freddie.' It was the last time he was to hear himself called by his Christian name by an adult for a long long time.

His ever-prevailing sense of curiosity lifted his feet, propelling him after matron to the dormitory he was to share with several other of the boys. Here he was given a little chest of drawers in which to put his meagre belongings.

Then, to his horror, he was taken firmly by the shoulder and pushed along the corridor to a bathroom where he was told in no uncertain terms to undress.

'But I already had a bath at Aunties',' he protested. 'In the tin tub in front of the fire last night. I **am** clean.'

Matron scowled at him. 'None of your lip,' she retorted. 'Get undressed. NOW!'

Holding back his indignation he was forced to undress infront of this strange woman. He was nine years old and he thought it was disgraceful that she should stand there watching him like...like a spider in a corner.

It wasn't the scrubbing with carbolic soap he objected to though he writhed and wriggled making it as difficult for her as possible - it was the de-lousing that raised his voice in furious protest. By the time she had finished with him his skin was raw and he was red all over.

She left him to put on the clean new school uniform telling him to come then immediately downstairs to the headmaster's office.

Freddie could read already quite well. He found no difficulty in locating the lavatory, the bathroom, the dining room, and finally Mr Nicholson's office. It was as clean and shiny as the rest of the place.

Freddie perched on the edge of the seat and listened. There seemed so many rules and times to observe that his head began to spin. He stared back at the master with glazed eyes.

'I don't expect you to take it all in at once,' Mr Nicholson told him. 'Someone will show you the ropes. The important thing is to be on time. We don't want half the police force out looking for you because you've forgotten the time. And...' For a moment his eyes looked right into young Freddie's soul, 'You must **never** leave the premises alone. Not ever! If you've got a problem you go to matron. If it's a really bad problem then she'll bring you to see me.'

Freddie sighed. How was he to know how long he'd been there? When would his father come back for him? Would he never again be allowed to run out on his own, free?

Mr Nicholson was ringing a tiny brass bell he'd picked up from the desk.

A tall boy with jet black hair and eyes appeared in an instant.

'This is Frederick Brayshay,' Mr Nicholson said. 'Take him to the playroom and introduce him to some of the boys.'

The first few weeks passed in a whirl of activity. There was so much to do. Each boy, however small, was given his duties. They shared in keeping the place clean; some of the rooms were vast and it was possible to see one's own reflection in the lino covered floors when it was your turn to wax and buff them: they washed up and made their own beds - in fact, between them, the boys did everything in the Home and garden except the actual cooking and washing.

Despite his earlier reaction to the rigid requirements of cleanliness, Freddie gradually came to realise that he was better cared for and better fed here than he had been for quite a long time back at Holme.

He liked being dressed the same as everyone else. It made him feel as if he belonged. For the first time in his life he met other boys who, like himself, had been adopted or abandoned. Some children had never had any parents they could remember whilst others recalled theirs with hate or pain.

Starting at his new school with the other boys from the Home was an unforgettable experience. They marched smartly in crocodile style down the main Bury New Road, into Leicester Road, and finally up to the school building: Leicester Road Boy's School, Lower Broughton; a massive red brick building.

Here he discovered for the first time how different people could be; there were many boys from Jewish families with their own peculiar beliefs and customs. In Salford, he now knew, there were children far worse off than they were living in a home for waifs and strays.

Wearing his uniform, marching through the town with the rest of the boys, he felt a strange pride. It was the beginning of a loyalty to his own kind that would stay with him for life.

If you had asked Fred then, he would have had no words to explain what was happening to him, but in reality he was discovering that he loved collective discipline. He had no time for those who whined or those who tried to sneak out of duties. He quickly found who he could trust, but to none did he ever speak about his family. It was just as if they had been wiped off the face of the earth.

Then one day he received a letter. It was from his father. He sat on a stone step in the sunshine reading the carefully hand printed symbols. His father told him little about what was happening but he did tell him that he loved him and missed him and that one day he would come and fetch him.

Freddie carefully folded the piece of paper and put it in his pocket. He was never going to lose it.

Once a month they were made to write home. It was impossible to tell what it was truly like there or how one really felt for every letter was vetted by Mr Nicholson before it left the building. Those boys who had no one to write to were given extra homework to occupy them while the other boys chewed at the ends of their pencils and struggled to produce a letter that would satisfy their Headmaster if not the recipient. No one was ever let off. Discipline was everything and Mr Nicholson was God.

The walls of the playroom were now covered with paintings of Snow White and The Seven Dwarfs. Each time he entered the room Freddie would look at his own contribution; he knew it was good, probably the best. One of the teachers at school told him to keep up his drawing, that one day it might be important to him. It was the first time since he left his old school that he had been given this kind of positive encouragement; he saw it no longer as a pastime, an idle doodling, but something important in its own right.

Freddie began to revel in learning; it came easily to him, the subjects he enjoyed brought pure happiness, those he didn't like he covered as quickly and efficiently as he could in order to get them out of the way.

Just when he had almost given up hoping, his Dad came to the Home. It was so unexpected Freddie stood and stared at him.

'How you doin'?' his Dad asked.

'I'm fine, Dad.' He gazed down at his clothes. He knew he looked smart and well cared for.

'I've permission to take you out for the day,' his Dad told him. 'Go and get your jacket.'

'What about Mr Nicholson?' Freddie found it hard to believe that he was actually being allowed out.

'It's okay. I've already arranged things with him. We're goin' to have dinner somewhere and then, if you like, I'll take you to the pictures.'

Freddie flew up the stairs. This was the best thing that had happened to him in...oh, he didn't know how long. His Dad was taking him out for the whole day.

They walked and talked for a long time. It was just as if they were visitors to Manchester, seeing it together for the first time. There were so many streets, so many shops and cinemas and splendid buildings.

In a small café they ordered dinner. The waitress was dressed in black and wore a white apron. Freddie's eyes followed her as she walked away. 'Cor, Dad! It's right posh in 'ere!' he exclaimed.

His father put his hand into his pocket, pulling out something he still concealed within his palm. He placed his clenched fist on the oilcloth covered table between them. The cloth had blue and white stripes with flowers around the edges.

'What you got, Dad?' Freddie knew it was something special. He recognised the expression on his Dad's face. He had always looked like that when, in the past, he made something for him.

'It's for you.' John Airey smiled. 'That's if you want it.'

Freddie stared at the wrist watch. He had never even dreamed of owning one. 'To keep?' he breathed.

'Yes. It's yours.'

'Oh, Dad!' He picked it up, turning it this way and that, finally he lifted it to his ear listening to the tiny tick, tick. 'Is this the right time?' he asked.

'Yes. Nearly one o'clock.'

'I can tell the time,' Freddie announced. Had his Dad forgotten how old he was?

'Of course!' His father smiled at him. 'You was always a bright lad. You're doin' alright, aren't you, Freddie? They treat you well?'

'Yes, Dad. Don't you worry about me.'

'I'm still goin' to fetch you back though, soon as I can.'

They stared at each other as the waitress placed two plates of steaming dinner in front of them.

Afterwards they made their way to the Picture House. The film being shown was 'It's In The Air' with George Formby. How they both laughed at his stupid antics. How Freddie enjoyed himself. It was one of those moments that made him say quietly to himself, 'I'm never goin' to forget this, not ever.'

Before a film started there was always music. Some people would start the singing and before you knew it, everyone was joining in. And then, during the interval in most cinemas a big electric organ would rise up out of the floor at the front of the stage like an underwater monster, and a man already seated at the keyboard would play all the old songs. Freddie felt as if he had stepped onto another planet.

When his Dad left him at the door of St George's Freddie stood watching him walk away. 'One day,' he whispered, 'he'll fetch me home again. I know he will.'

Looking at his watch now firmly strapped around his wrist he walked slowly into the building. He was going to show it to the rest of the boys. Wait till they saw what he'd got!

The George Formby film wasn't the only one he saw. In the Home they had a projector and as the building next door was used by Gainsborough Films, somehow or other they were able to borrow from time to time those films considered suitable for the boys to watch. They didn't care **what** they saw, they loved the lot. At school they knew there were boys who'd never ever been to the pictures.

School holidays were gloriously, wonderfully different. All forty two of the boys were taken to stay at the Old School House over at Fleetwood. There were no lessons and very few chores. They spent hours on the beach or playing in the park, creating a world of steam engines, trams and buses. Who needed toys when they had their imaginations?

In Fleetwood they were taken sometimes to watch films at the Art Cinema. There were cartoons that had them rocking in their seats; Old Mother Riley who everyone knew was a man dressed up, Laurel and Hardy and Buster Keaton; they didn't seem to be a nuisance to anyone, no one complained at the din they made; it never occurred to the children that because they were part of a church charity people looked upon them more tolerantly, they only knew it felt good to be there.

Memories of Cliviger and Holme came less frequently, there was so much to do, to see, to learn, and they had each other - in a way they were their own family, only they didn't know how to put it into words.

It was during holiday time that rumours of war reached the ears of the Home boys.

Every adult, with bated breath, seemed to be waiting for something to happen. When it didn't, things gradually returned to normal. There was no bombing, no invasion, no gas insidiously creeping round corners threatening to terminate their lives.

All this, however, made little impression on the children in the Home, and as it made no difference to their lives it was dismissed.

Sometimes they overheard adults talking in hushed or angry tones; sometimes the radio with its crackles and hisses could be heard from outside the Headmaster's room telling of battles and fears of invasion; 'paper boys' at street corners yelled the latest news. If the boys at St George's had actually been asked, they would have readily told anyone that they were looking forward to a **real** war with bombs and aeroplanes and soldiers marching about everywhere.

The hot summer continued. It had begun to feel as if it would go on forever. Passing a paddock one day a group of the lads paused to look at the horses.

'If we have a war we'll have to eat them,' one lad announced. 'In a war you have to eat horse meat.'

'I won't,' Freddie said. 'I'd die first.'

The master gave a couple of them a push. 'Come on you lot. If you want some free time before you go to bed you'd better get a move on.'

Freddie lead the way, eager to reach the playground of the Home ahead of the rest. He jumped on a swing and began to push it higher and higher into the air. He could see for miles.

A terrible scream suddenly shattered the air. It went on and on and on. Freddie hauled his swing to a halt and looked in the direction of the see-saws. Aspinall was standing there, hands over his face, blood running between his fingers.

Everyone stared, frozen with horror - and then in a bunch they approached the screaming boy. Surrounding him, the whole gang of lads attempted to quieten him, to find out what had happened. The boy continued to scream.

They knew they **had** to do **something**. But he wouldn't move his hands away from his face and he wouldn't stop yelling in order to tell them what was wrong. Finally, dragging him still screaming, they took him to the Sick Room.

It was not until much later they learned he had lost his eye. A strange twist of fate had caused the see-saw to hit the boy as he had played on it, dislodging one eye from its socket.

He seemed to be gone from the Home for a long time. When he returned he wore a patch over the empty hole.

The lads crowded around. 'Let's look,' they pleaded. 'Go on, let's have a look.'

'Not till I get me new eye in.' He backed away. 'Then you can all 'ave a look.'

'How can you get a **new** eye? You bust it didn't you?' One of the older boys looked at him suspiciously.

'I'm gettin' a glass eye,' he announced proudly. 'I can 'ave it any colour I like.' He was enjoying the unusual position of popularity to which he had suddenly been elevated.

Freddie was fascinated. 'What colour are you 'avin'?'

'The same as the other.' Aspinall grinned. 'I did think about 'avin' a red one but the doc said it would look funny.'

They waited impatiently to see the glass eye. Freddie wondered if he could use it as a marble.

Aspinall gloried in the attention he received when he returned from the hospital wearing his new brown eye. Although, he assured them, he couldn't see with it, he was still immensely proud.

The first time he took it out and glared at them with one empty socket, Freddie thought he would faint. But in the end it became a joke. If Aspinall was about to be punished or found out for some trick he'd played, he would suddenly groan, lower his head, and a second later he would be facing his adversary with an expression of mock pain on his face, the glass eye held in his hand.

No amount of reprimands or threats ever cured him of this revolting habit. Even Mr Nicholson gave up on him. Perhaps he thought losing an eye was punishment enough.

The war was imminent, but still it made no difference to the running of the Home or what was expected of them. Mr Nicholson was as strict as always and the cane, when you were unfortunate enough to merit it, was dealt with the same measured lashes accompanied by the same reprimands. The boys hoped for a miracle - even that Mr Nicholson might be called up - but everything seemed to go on just the same.

And then something did happen. They learned that several of their playmates from school now had a very special label - German Jews.

'They'll put them away,' one lad said. 'I heard my Dad talking about it. They're the enemy, they might turn on you in the night and knife you in the back.'

Freddie stared at him as if he had gone mad. How could people you'd known all your life change into monsters knifing their own friends and neighbours?

Wolfgang Mozart, champion runner of the school, came to him in the cloakroom. 'I have to go away,' he said simply.

Freddie knew Wolfgang's father was a German though he owned a respectable jewellers shop at the corner of the street.

'Are you goin' back to Germany?' he asked. He thought it might be fun to travel on a huge ship right across the sea.

But Wolfgang shook his head. 'No. We are to be interned. It's a sort of prison where we have to stay until the war is over.'

'But you haven't done anything wrong,' Freddie said. 'It isn't fair.'

'They are afraid we might. I have to go.' He pulled a pair of running shoes from his locker and stared at them in silence for a few moments.

Freddie also looked at them somewhat enviously; none of the boys from the Home owned such a pair of shoes.

'Here.' Impulsively Wolfgang thrust them into his hands. 'You have them. I shall not be allowed to run or compete where I am going.'

For a long time Freddie stayed looking at the shoes, trying to imagine what it must be like to be locked up. He was very very glad he was in the Home. Sometimes, it seemed, it was better **not** to have a family.

September 3rd: War was officially declared the day gas masks came to the Home. Everyone had to have one. You weren't allowed to go anywhere at all outside the building without one. It was carried to and from school each day in a cardboard box slung around each boy's neck on a cord.

Using the gas mask became part of morning assembly. If you took too long to get it out of the box and onto your head when the whistle blew you were made to stay in during playtime and practise over and over again.

Adults smiled less often and there was a kind of desperate feeling in the way they joked and spent their leisure time.

To the boys the war at last brought change; everything became exciting, there was a perpetual air of anticipation; school and lessons were suspended.

That same evening the boys were called into the playroom. Matron told them to sit cross-legged on the floor. 'Mr Nicholson has a very important announcement to make. Be very quiet when he comes in and listen carefully.'

They didn't need to be told to behave. Mr Nicholson had filled each young heart with dread, his authority and discipline were absolute; no boy ever dared to defy him or question what he was told to do when the order, direct or indirect, came from their awesome Headmaster.

Freddie fidgeted on the polished lino. He could sense something tremendous was about to happen. Perhaps Mr Nicholson was leaving. Maybe he **had** been called-up. He tried to suppress the tingle of excitement running through his body. If Mr Nicholson went, what would happen to them? This was their home. Who else was there to look after them?

At last he came, just when the children felt they couldn't bear the suspense a minute longer. Looking more fierce and forbidding than ever, he deliberately moved his eyes from one young face to the next before finally addressing them.

Freddie tried to stare back. He knew it was important to look at him directly, otherwise he was sure to think you had been up to no good. Did his eyes hesitate a little longer on Freddie than the rest? He held his breath praying he wouldn't be singled out. He couldn't remember having done anything wrong for days.

Then in a voice more stern than usual he made his announcement: 'Because of the war it has been decided for your own safety that all the children in the area are to be evacuated. You will leave at six thirty tomorrow morning. There will be no home work tonight and no jobs. I want you to clear up all your things. You will each be given a large brown paper bag for your personal belongings.'

The boys stared at each other. Where were they going? And who was going to look after them? Would they still go to school?

Mr Nicholson raised his voice. 'Get moving then.'

Their packing completed they ate their last meal together. With tongues wagging they speculated on where they were going. The sense of excitement was contagious. It was the biggest thing that had ever happened to them. They hadn't the slightest idea who would look after them; they had no clothes of their own, not even a pair of pyjamas; everything they wore belonged to the Home.

Spending their last few hours in the playroom the excitement caught fire. Suddenly they WANTED to go. They all felt sure something wonderful would happen once they got away from this place.

The lady who worked in the kitchen brought them pieces of ginger bread and milk. 'You poor mites. Eat this quickly, and don't tell a soul I gave it to you.' She lifted her apron and wiped at her watery eyes. 'God bless you,' she sobbed, backing out of the room.

The boys pounced on this unexpected treat. Someone suggested they sang all the songs that they knew to give them heart. They tried to turn it into a farewell party. With no adult to supervise them they yelled their way through .'Underneath The Spreading Chestnut Tree,' and 'Run Rabbit Run.'

Freddie went to take a last look at the paintings on the walls in the playroom. He hoped someone would let his Dad know he had gone away, it would be awful if he came for him and found he wasn't there anymore.

Chapter 6

EVACUATION TO FLEETWOOD

September 8th 1939

From the declaration of war it had, in reality, taken only five days for the evacuation to be organised. In clean clothes, clutching their brown paper bags, the boys marched crocodile style to the railway station; each had a red band across his chest with his name and St George's Home printed on it. Their gas masks hung around their necks, familiarity now having made them as much part of their dress as the short grey trousers they wore. For many of them it was to be their first journey in a train.

The station was packed with a seething jumble of people. Some were crying, everyone seemed to be shouting to everyone else. Mothers hugged their children issuing last minute instructions to write, to be good, to come back soon.

Everyone was saying the war would soon be over. No one believed it.

The station master and porters tried in vain to restore order, but it was impossible. Never in the history of the railway had there been such an exodus.

The Home boys, free from control - for it was impossible for the master in charge to keep an eye on all forty two boys amidst so many - slipped quietly away, diving between people's legs, peering into the waiting rooms, the toilets, the ticket office. They were wild with excitement and totally failed to understand why some children looked so miserable or cried so bitterly.

Before the announcement came, they had already heard the distant sound of the steam engine and ran out to the edge of the platform to peer down the line, watching the hissing, steaming, shining monster arrive with all its impressive splendour. They could even **smell** the steam.

'All aboard. All aboard. Every child must get on the train. NOW!'

Some hung back with frightened fingers clutching at their mother's skirts. But the children from the Home clambered up the steps eager to experience whatever was in store for them.

There was so much to see they had no intention of sitting down sedately in a carriage. They streamed down the corridors, climbing over suitcases, squeezing past hoards of bodies. Where was the lavatory? Nobody seemed to know. The boys wondered if they could pee out of the windows.

Freddie squashed his nose against the glass, seeing with a sense of shock the tation to move before realising that it was, in fact, the train pulling out, taking them to, 'who knows where?'

One word began to rustle through the children packed tightly into every conceivable space - FLEETWOOD. **We're going to Fleetwood.**

Freddie looked at Aspinall who stared back with his one good eye. 'That's where we go every holiday. It's by the sea. We're goin' to live by the sea.'

They grinned at each other. 'Do you suppose we'll go to the Old School House?' Aspinall looked hopeful. 'It's a hundred times better than the Home.'

Nothing, however, had prepared them for the surprise awaiting them on their arrival: tired and considerably dirtier than when they started out, they were met at the station by a group of important looking adults and taken en masse to a welcoming party that set their eyes wide in surprise and delight.

The atmosphere was one of carnival. Walking past the North Euston Hotel they were encouraged by smiling ladies wearing an impressive collection of coloured hats to be brave, to keep their chins up, to keep walking. Repeatedly they were assured they would soon be there - wherever 'there' was.

Finally they arrived at the Marine Hall to find colourful flags and bunting draped all over the outside of the building.

Evacuees from Salford arriving at Fleetwood only five days after war was declared. Fred is fifth from the right carrying his gas mask

Inside were more trimmings and a man seated at an electric organ playing songs. The sight of tables bowed down with food provided by the kindly people of the town made their mouths water. Encouraged over and over again to help themselves, the boys ate until several of them were sick.

No one told them off, the strange adults only murmured about nerves and the stress of the journey.

Gradually people started to organise things; children were handed over to adults and taken away. The hall began to empty.

From the moment they had arrived at the station the boys from St George's had seen no sign of their master or matron; no one had any apparent interest in who they were or where they had come from. One by one they began to remove their bands of identity.

Freddie realised with a strange sense of loss that his companions were rapidly disappearing in the hands of strangers. Un-noticed, he pulled off the red band looped around his body and pushed it with the address card still pinned to it into a dark corner.

Suddenly he was scooped up with two other boys he had never met before and taken outside by a fat vague lady who asked them politely to follow her.

There didn't seem anything else to do, unless they wanted to stay all night in the hall amongst the debris of food and paper plates.

They stopped outside the door of an old Victorian type building in a row of similar houses situated in a street close to the sea front. The lady looked down at them and smiled. 'This is your new home,' she said. 'And I'm Mrs Williams. You'll be staying with me.'

She lead them through a clean tidy hallway and up the staircase. In a room where three small beds had been squashed into a space meant for one, she told them this was where they were to sleep.

'You can put your things in there.' She pointed to the chest of drawers. 'There's one for each of you.'

Freddie claimed the bed next to the window. From there he could watch the people going up the hill to the sea front.

'Come on,' she said. 'Put your clothes away.'

'I don't have any.' Freddie looked at her curiously, wondering what she would do about it.

'No clothes?' Her voice rose an octave.

'That's right.'

'Where are they? Did you lose them?' she questioned.

The idea suddenly struck him as a good one. If he said they were lost perhaps she wouldn't try to contact Mr Nicholson and he could just go on staying there in an ordinary house with ordinary people.

'I must have,' he replied. 'I've only got those.' He indicated the brown paper bag containing the toys, crayons, books, and things his father had once made for him.

'Oh dear!' She looked bewildered for a few minutes.

Freddie decided that maybe he should help her out. 'It's alright. I could stay in bed on the day you do the washing. I don't mind.'

'Of course you can't!' For a moment she looked distracted, then brightening she said, 'I'll have to try and get you some tomorrow.'

They quickly found out where the bathroom was and obediently washed their hands before running downstairs to the kitchen.

Mrs Williams had set three places at the table. It was covered in a yellow patterned piece of oilcloth. A small vase of flowers stood in the centre.

'Sit down please.' She didn't seem to know how to treat children. It was almost as if they were in a café and she was the waitress.

Freddie looked at the other two boys and grinned. 'What's your names?' he asked.

It was the beginning of a friendship which was to last for the next two months as they roamed around Fleetwood completely free from any parental or adult discipline.

Each morning Mrs Williams gave them breakfast and a packet of sandwiches to take with them for lunch. She never pried into where they had been or what they had done. 'Be back by six,' was all she said. 'Have a lovely day.'

She also gave them enough pocket money each morning so that they could go down to the docks and catch the Ferry across the river Wyre to Knott End. On good days they spent hours and hours on the beach fishing for crabs and playing games.

The shore had been rapidly fortified with concrete pill boxes and protected from possible invaders by rolls and rolls of barbed wire, but wherever there was a place left unprotected the boys would find it, crawling through on their bellies, playing at fighting the German soldiers they had never seen.

Digging in the sand they made castles and tunnels; sometimes they would pull off their boots and socks and play in the shallow water, watching in a kind of fascination as the waves rolled in over their feet. The Home, to Freddie, seemed a million miles away.

From there they could see Blackpool, and sometimes, when it was too cold or wet for crabbing, they would catch a tram in Lord Street and ride all the way to the Blackpool Tower.

Freddie, standing gazing up at it, wondered at its size and perfection. He longed to climb to the top. Was it the cost or the height that prevented him from exploring? He never knew, but something always stopped him short of this adventure.

Mrs Williams kept her promise, and Freddie found himself for the first time since going to St George's wearing ordinary clothes. He had become so used to his blue knitted uniform jersey with its red collar that it had become almost like a second skin. He stared down at the new check shirt and green jumper she had just given him and stroked his front.

'Do you like it?' she asked. 'Is it alright?'

It was funny how she tried to please him. 'It's lovely,' he said. 'Thank you.'

'Good. I expect you miss your family. Your mummy and daddy?' For the first time she looked at him with a curiosity he found unnerving.

He thought fast. He didn't want her to find out about the Home, not ever. 'Oh, I'm used to being on my own,' he said. 'I like it here.'

She tried several times to get him to talk about his previous life but he was a genius at avoiding the truth or diverting her attention elsewhere. Without her realising it, he outwitted her every time.

There was so much to see, to learn, to absorb - strange new sights, buildings, ships, and the throbbing aeroplanes which had begun to go over the town at night.

Things even smelled different. Touching, hearing, tasting, seeing, all their senses were being utilised to the full in the wonderful discovery of learning first hand about the world that now surrounded them.

Freddie was curled up on the settee reading a comic one evening when the door bell rang.

'Can you answer it, please?' Mrs Williams was upstairs washing her hair in the bathroom.

The boys looked at each other. 'Oh, I'll go.' Freddie stood up. He had automatically taken over the role of leader.

He turned the key and pulled open the door. A man wearing a dark blue mac with a white band across his body and another round his sleeve looked down at Freddie.

'Hello, sonny. Is the lady of the house in?' he asked.

Freddie felt a quiver of doom. He didn't know who the man was but he was sure he brought only bad news.

'She can't see anybody now.' He tried to close the door but the man neatly placed his foot inside the door frame.

'You'd better call her,' he said. 'I'm the billeting officer.'

'Who is it, Freddie?'

The man heard her and looked expectantly at the boy. Reluctantly Freddie shouted up the stairs. 'It's a man. He wants to see you.'

Slowly she came down to meet him winding a towel around her head. 'Yes?'

Freddie watched and waited.

'I'm the billeting officer, ma'am. I believe you may have some boys here from St George's Home for Waifs and Strays.'

Mrs Williams looked puzzled. 'You must be mistaken. I only have evacuees.'

'Do you have one called Frederick Brayshay?'

Her eyes met Freddie's. Please, he wanted to say, tell him it's not me. Send him away.

But the man knew, even before she said anything he was moving towards Freddie. 'It's you, sonny, isn't it? They've been looking everywhere for you. You'll have to come along with me.'

'Does he have to go?' Mrs Williams was looking really upset now.

'Yes, ma'am. He's to join the rest of the boys from the Home.'

Freddie went upstairs to pack his things once more in the brown paper bag. He left the clothes she had given him on the bed.

'Won't you be coming back?' one of the boys asked.

He shook his head. He knew Mr Nicholson would never let him out again. Not on his own. Not ever.

The man was kind. He kept on talking to Freddie as they walked along the pavement. He seemed to be trying to make it easy for him. 'All your old mates will be there. They've rounded them all up now, you're the last. You'll enjoy seeing all your friends won't you?'

Freddie didn't reply.

He said, 'We've got to go to the old Military Hospital in Coniston Avenue.'

It was a long walk. Freddie trailed behind him, wondering if he dared slip away back to kind Mrs Williams.

But it wasn't any use, the man kept pausing, waiting for him to catch up, chivvying him along, telling him how much he would enjoy it when he got there.

The building stood at the end of the avenue. They walked past rows of lovely houses each neatly contained within their own stone walls with square lawns and flower borders.

The sight of the military hospital was like receiving a cold shower of water after the gentle lull of the avenue with its trees and nice houses; square, derelict, the building stood stark and grey against the sky.

Nothing had prepared him for this. He waited in the dank gloom of the reception hall. There were no electric lights, only a small yellow gas lamp hanging in a sickly glow from the ceiling. As he moved forward he looked down the corridor and saw how unkempt the place was. Surely the soldiers who had once stayed here in the olden days must have got better just to get away? How could the military keep a place like this?

Then a door opened and he saw in an instant all the old familiar faces. 'Spider! Billie! Teddy! Ken!'

They rushed to greet each other. 'Where were you? When did they get you? How long have you been here?' Everyone was talking at once. They dragged him into a room, telling him of their adventures, the places where they had each ended up after leaving the grand reception on the day of their arrival.

The Old Military Hospital   Coniston Avenue   Fleetwood

(The building has long been demolished)

84

For two whole months the authorities had lost contact with all forty two boys from the Home. Then Mr Nicholson had arrived in Fleetwood and started the business of rounding them up.

From somewhere funds were made available and the boys were put to work mending, cleaning, scrubbing, struggling to create cleanliness and order out of the awful mess they encountered in their new 'home'. There was no running water and no electricity.

This was worse, much worse than St George's. It was like a long terrible nightmare that wouldn't go away.

One day they were informed that they would be going to Beech Road School to continue their education.

Freddie never found out why they were segregated from the local children. Perhaps there were just too many for the teachers to handle. For whatever reason, it was decided that the evacuee children would be taught in the mornings and the local children in the afternoons.

The enmity between the two groups began on the very first day. Some of the local children, deprived of morning school, hung around the playground railings chanting at the 'foreigners.'

Fights frequently broke out, and every time the Home boys returned to the Military Hospital bruised, bleeding, or with clothes torn, they were lined up and beaten by Nicholson.

They stood outside his door hearing the swishing of the cane, imagining the tingle of it on their own flesh long before they stepped over the threshold into his study.

Freddie's eyes started at his shiny shoes, they moved slowly up over the grey striped trousers with the knife edged creases, they paused at the top of his trousers where his braces could be seen neatly buttoned - two on either side; his eyes examined the plain but immaculately ironed shirt, the perfectly knotted tie, and finally, because there was no where else for his eyes to go, he looked at the thin lean face with the stiff black moustache.

'Brayshay, again! Are you never going to learn? Clothes cost good money. There's a war on in case it has escaped your attention. You are a disgrace to the Home. You bring shame on us all. You are a hooligan. Do you hear me? A **hooligan!**'

Fred looked at him unflinching. You must never show any sign of weakness before the enemy.

'Take down your trousers.'

This was really bad, usually it was a few strokes of the cane across the palm of one hand. He gritted his teeth and thought about what he would do to those kids the next day who were responsible for his punishment. At each lash his determination to grind them into the ground grew stronger.

He had earned the label 'disruptive.' He now hated arithmetic; he wasn't any good at it and the teacher's way of trying to make the slow ones learn was to ridicule them in front of the others. Freddie's reaction was one of bravado which unfortunately only attracted more adverse attention.

But his art lessons were something different. Miss Clayton, who taught art, quickly recognised which children had natural talent and she made sure they had the best of the materials available to work with. Because of the war, the paints they used were usually poster colours that were impossible to mix smoothly, and the paper was sheets of old wallpaper cut from a roll. But from somewhere she managed to provide Freddie with paints and paper that made it possible for him to produce work of which he was justly proud. He needed to further his skills and found himself spending more and more of his free time drawing. He admired and respected Miss Clayton more than anyone else in his present world. In her class he was the shining pupil.

At first Freddie had been quite envious of the boys in Fleetwood he saw who wore no shoes or socks, it demonstrated a sense of freedom which was completely outside the experience of the boys within the Home. It was only later that he learned they wore none because they had none.

November 29th 1940 the first real bombing began across the water. Because there were no lights in the bedrooms the boys were sent to bed early. At least this way there was no problem with 'black-out', they didn't have to have the windows covered with old blankets like most people, blocking out the fresh air, stifling them. But it was impossible to sleep. For one thing it was too hot, for another the smell from eight boys crowded into a small room which had been intended as a ward for two made things at times almost unbearable.

Crowding at the window they could see all the way over to Liverpool. It was like a fantastic fireworks display that just went on and on. The whole of the horizon was lit up. It never occurred to any of them that anyone might get hurt. The excitement was infectious; they yelled and cheered as they watched the results of each explosion.

'Look at that! Did you see that?'

Freddie pointed. 'Look over there. Them's incendiary bombs. They make everythin' catch fire.'

A boom shook the windows. 'Wow! How about that?' Spider shouted. 'That's the loudest yet.'

It was better than any film they had ever seen. The only disappointment being that they were forced to watch it from **inside** the Old Military Hospital.

They knew that Mr Nicholson went out each evening after they had been sent to bed. Sometimes the braver ones would then creep downstairs, avoiding matron and Mr Smith, playing games in the shadows, risking the punishment of getting caught.

One evening Spider found a bubble in a window pane. It fascinated him. He leaned his face against it squinting through the glass with one eye. Then one day from somewhere he acquired a bottle. Rushing to the window he placed the flat end of it against the glass bubble.

'Hey! Look!,' he shouted. 'It's like a telescope. It magnifies everythin'. You can see for miles...well... streets away, at least.'

Freddie grabbed the bottle. For a moment he was silent, swivelling it round, watching something the others couldn't see.

'What you lookin' at?' Spider tried to grab it back.

'It's Mr Nicholson. I can see him. He's walkin' down the next street. Hey! He's goin' to the pub.'

'Let's look. Let me look.'

Each boy in turn peered through the glass bottle. It was an incredible feeling to be spying on the Headmaster knowing he couldn't possibly see them, unaware that he was being watched.

It became part of their nightly ritual to stand in turn at the window and watch him walk to the pub. It was as if knowing his weakness gave them a superiority over him. His threats and punishment never again held the same sting. As he beat them they had only to picture him through the bottom of the glass bottle and the pain seemed less and the indignity melted away.

But the indignity of the tar-coated rain capes could not be dealt with so easily. One of the trawler captains had made a gift of such a cape to each boy in the Home. They seemed to weigh a ton, hanging in a black shapeless huddle almost to their ankles. Mr Nicholson, fearful of offending this unexpected benefactor - and looking for further 'kindnesses'- insisted they were worn each day as the boys marched down the road to school. No matter what the weather, they were forced to wear the capes.

The derision from the local children was bad enough, the discomfort almost intolerable in hot weather, but by far the worse thing was the tar coating itself; in summer it melted leaving brown or black smears on everything. No matter how careful you were, by the time you returned to the Home at least some part of the anatomy, or even worse, one's clothing, was stained from the tar.

Mr Nicholson would glare down his sharp straight nose, twitch his moustache and tell them to go at once and wash and then see him after in his room. His thrashings were accompanied by a lecture on ungratefulness and the virtues of being clean.

'I'll kill that captain if I ever see him,' Billie groaned one evening after a particularly severe caning. 'He must be a maniac.'

'Or a sadist,' Freddie said. He'd just learned the word and was finding ample practice for it.

'He drinks with Mr Nicholson at the pub,' Ken announced. 'He must have offered to buy the capes for us one night when they got drunk.'

Spider looked interested. 'How do you know they drink together?'

'I saw them one time through the end of the bottle. They met at the corner and were talking to each other.'

'But he never comes here.' Billie was lying on his stomach to prevent his rear end taking any more suffering.

'We could go to his boat.' Ken looked around waiting for their reaction. 'If we made a hole in the side of it that would make it sink and then they'd all be drowned.'

They stared at each other, appalled and fascinated by the idea.

Freddie shook his head. 'We'd only get caught and thrashed even harder. We wouldn't dare. Anyway it isn't worth it. They might put us in prison. There must be another way.'

'Then we have to sabotage the capes,' Ken announced. 'We simply put them out of action.'

'How?' Billie asked.

No one knew. Whatever they planned it had to be when they were in a situation which left them above suspicion.

'How about a fire?' Freddie suggested.

'We might all get burned alive.' Ken sighed. 'It isn't going to be easy.'

It was several days before the solution presented itself to Freddie. Quite by accident, while cleaning the store cupboard off the kitchen he discovered a jar of glue. He went to lift it down from the shelf but it was stuck fast. The more he pulled the tighter it seemed to hold. It became a challenge, a battle between him and the jar and he was determined not to be beaten. It must have been there for simply ages, he decided. No one could have known about it or else they just hadn't tried very hard to remove it.

Slowly the thought came. If no one knew it was there, then no one was going to miss it. He climbed off the stool and went in search of a knife. The kitchen was empty. Every boy was busy somewhere in the building doing his chores.

It released its hold finally, bringing with it a chunk of the shelf. Freddie expertly covered the damage with a finger smeared in wet vim; he then placed a pot of jam over the top to be on the safe side.

Slipping the glue jar under his jumper he ran to the room he shared with Spider, Billie, Ken, and Aspinall. He pushed the jar under his bed and returned to complete his jobs.

When they all finally met up in the playroom he was bubbling with excitement. 'I've worked out how to get rid of the capes,' he announced, feeling very pleased with himself.

'How? How?' They all wanted to know.

'We wait until we see old Nicholson goin' to the pub, then two of you have to keep matron and Mr Smith busy while the rest of us pour glue over the capes.'

'Glue? Where? How?' Ken asked, falling backwards over a chair in his excitement.

'I've already got it. A big jar of it. We'll never be able to wear the capes again. The only way they'll ever come apart afterwards is if they cut them.'

'But Mr Nicholson will know someone's done it.'

'No he won't. The capes are always kept in the cupboard under the stairs. There's a shelf on the wall above them, I've already checked. We're going to make it look as if this old jar of glue just fell off the shelf and ran all over the capes. The only thing is, we have to make sure it gets on every single one.'

That night they crowded at the window, craning their necks, looking for Nicholson. Billie nearly fell out as he insisted on opening a window and leaning right over the ledge in an endeavour to be the first to see the Headmaster walking away. Someone hauled him back threatening him with murder if he ruined their plans.

As soon as they saw the dapper figure with his rolled up umbrella striding down the far street which lead to the pub, they dashed downstairs.

It had been decided that to ensure Matron was kept busy, Spider would suddenly curl up feigning stomach pains and Ken would run to get her while Billie went for Mr Smith.

While Spider writhed on the floor the rest of them, armed with pieces of cardboard, crept into the cupboard and began to smear the glue on the tar coating of the capes, pressing them down in a heap. The smell from the glue was terrible.

A few minutes later they backed out and Freddie threw the empty jar in on top of the ruined capes.

Running as if the devil himself was after them they made for the playroom. They wanted to meet in their bedroom to discuss the escapade but knew that this would cause suspicion. No boy ever went to bed until he was ordered to do so. They had already decided on no account to speak to any of the other boys about what they had done; some of the younger ones could not be trusted to keep a secret. Interrogated by Mr Nicholson, threatened with a caning, they might break down.

They were quietly reading when matron came in through the door. Spider had been ordered to spend the night in the little room set aside for children who were ill. He dared not risk a too sudden recovery - it might arouse suspicion.

Freddie felt a moment of compassion, he guessed Spider would be forced to drink the dreaded caster oil. It was matron's remedy for everything.

She stood now eyeing the boys suspiciously. 'You're incredibly quiet for once.'

They stared back hoping she wasn't a mind-reader.

'Oh, dear me, NO!' Her voice filled with dismay. She came into the room advancing on the older boys. 'I hope you're not all sickening for whatever Henry Spiller's got.'

Of course they all knew she meant Spider, but no one dared offer an explanation.

'Stick out your tongues.' She stood close to Freddie. 'You first.'

'I'm feeling fine,' Freddie said. 'Really I am.'

'Me too!' Billie jumped up.

'Show me your tongue.' Matron peered at them, searching for evidence of some dreaded disease.

'Wait here,' she ordered. 'Don't any of you leave this room.'

'You know what she's going to do?' one of them said.

'CASTOR OIL!' They all groaned.

Freddie and his pals would have liked to explain the situation to the other boys in the Home, to lessen the ordeal, to help them see that it was a small price to pay for never having to wear a cape again. Helpless, the culprits stared at each other.

Matron returned, doling out a spoonful of the oil to each boy, watching until she saw his throat move as he swallowed. It was curious how fussy she could be about germs and yet expected them all to lick at the same spoon.

They never found out who discovered the capes glued together. Mr Smith simply told them next morning that they would no longer be wearing them. A cheer went up from some of the boys. Freddie and his sabotage team kept very quiet.

They were into summer when Mr Nicholson one evening after dinner made an important announcement. He didn't, he explained, believe in the boys being idle for weeks on end during school holidays.

That was a joke, someone muttered, with all the work they were expected to do inside and outside the old hospital, who had time to be idle?

'I have arranged,' the Master said, 'for you boys to go and help out with the pea harvesting. For the next two weeks you will be pea picking. A vehicle will collect you each morning and return you each evening. You will stay together and you will NOT, for any reason, leave the field where you will be working. Is that understood?'

'Yes sir.' The boys looked at each other in wonder. It sounded fantastic. Escape from this dump for two whole weeks.

They'd get to spend every day in the country and all they had to do was pick a few peas.

The reality was, however, a little different. They were collected each morning at seven thirty and bundled into the back of an open truck. This might have been fun except that often it was cold and windy and there was always the fear of over-balancing and ending up in the road with your head split wide open.

Even harder to bear were the back aching hours and hours of picking the full green pods of peas. From time to time the farmer would walk past calling to them to make a greater effort. Wasn't he paying them for doing it? he asked.

Of course they never saw the money, not one penny of it, Nicholson, they decided, spent the lot on drink. There was only one compensation, they ate as many peas as they could cram into their mouths when no one was looking.

That first night the peas caught up with them. First one and then another boy emitted a loud explosion of wind.

'I can beat you,' Spider said, farting loudly. 'How about that?'

'I can do a bigger one.' Freddie demonstrated.

'What about this then,' Billie yelled. 'Try an' beat that one.'

'I know, let's have a competition,' Ken suggested. 'Let's see who can make the longest loudest fart.'

Between giggles and farts they failed to hear the door open. The smell from that hot overcrowded room nearly knocked matron right off her feet.

'What is the meaning of this?' she demanded.

But no one heard her. The noise and laughter was too great.

'Stop that at once!' she shrieked.

Spider let out his best ever fart and then found himself looking up into those cold blue eyes. He almost stopped breathing altogether. 'I...I can't help it matron.'

Another explosion vibrated through the air. 'Sorry, matron. I can't help it either,' Ken giggled. 'It's the peas.'

'Oh, is that so? We'll see about that!' She flounced out of the room.

'She can't stop us,' Freddie said. 'It's natural. When you've got wind inside you it's got to come out.'

'I bet you she's gone to get old Nicholson,' Billie said.

'He'll be at the pub,' Spider told him hopefully. 'Anyway there's nothing they can do about it. You can't help having wind.'

But their luck had run out. Mr Nicholson had not gone to the pub, he was standing now in the doorway with such a look of rage on his face that it froze their hearts. The last unfortunate comment of Spider's had been overheard.

'All of you, pull down your pyjama trousers.'

It was the worse beating they had received so far. When he left the room, no one spoke, no one even whimpered; pulling the bed clothes over their heads each boy tried in his own way to come to terms with the unfairness of the world in which he lived.

In each heart a hatred, such as they had never felt before, burned for the master who had no heart.

From the 7th of September 1940 to the end of May 1941 the Luftwaffe dropped some 46,000 tons of high explosive and 110,000 incendiaries, a total of 54,420 tons of bombs; 40,000 civilians were killed and 86,000 seriously injured. Two million houses were destroyed or damaged.

British industrial production and tonnage moving through the ports was, however, not seriously affected, and internal communications continued without disruption; so although in parts of England many children had been returned to their homes after the initial exodus of September/October 1939, the children in Fleetwood were thought to be safe and it was decided that they should remain where they were.

A rumour began to circulate throughout the Home. They were leaving the Old Military Hospital and being taken to The Old School House where they had spent each summer holiday when they were at St George's in Salford.

Could it be true? Was it possible the place they loved most of all was to be their new home?

'I expect someone's reported the rats,' Billie said in a nonchalant way.

'What rats?' everyone asked.

'The rats that live here in this stinking old building,' Billie stated.

'But there aren't any,' Aspinall said, looking around with some trepidation. 'I've never seen any.'

'THEY don't know that,' Billie said. 'But I expect when they came to inspect this place it **looked** as if rats live here. It's damned well cold enough and damp enough.' He pointed to the black mildew on the peeling walls.

Freddie gazed at him with admiration. Had Billie spread the story about rats to the teachers at school?

He never let on, not to any of them, but they soon learned that the rumour about the move was true. They were going to spend the rest of their time in Fleetwood at the Old School House.....

The Old School House (The Testimonial School) Fleetwood
Demolished in the sixties

There followed nearly eighteen months of tranquillity - if one ignored the dropping of bombs, the nightly roar of the planes and the continued battles with the local children - the boys of the Home settled down into a routine, and in a fashion they learned.

The classrooms of the Old School House became their dormitories as before the war, each boy sleeping on a straw-filled palliasse placed directly on the floor.

It seemed to be in the middle of the night that the first sounds of the trams which rattled above ground were heard by the boys, magnified ten fold through their pillows. But, like everything else, they eventually adapted to the rumblings and learned, despite the racket, to sleep undisturbed.

Although birthdays were recognised within the Home and a cake made in the kitchen to mark the occasion, many of the boys had little else to help them mark the years. It was as if they had become isolated in a world of their own.

This year, however, Fred was determined to make something of becoming twelve years old. His Dad had written to him enclosing a postal order for two pounds. He'd persuaded matron to make a special tea and he had spent some of his own money on sweets he intended to share with everyone - he'd bought lemon sherbet, licorice sticks and aniseed balls at twenty five for a ha'penny. Rationing had started in January of that year - first it was bacon, sugar and butter, then in March meat was included and tea was added to the list in July. Times, everyone said, were hard.

Undaunted, Freddie made a banner announcing his birthday, and suspended it from the ceiling.

The last thing he had expected was that Mr Nicholson would recognise this as Freddie's special day. But there he stood in the doorway looking at the brightly painted banner; it was part of a roll of old wall paper and reached from one side of the room to the other.

The boys were playing musical bumps to an old gramophone record and did not at first notice the arrival of their headmaster.

'Brayshay?' At the sound of his voice everyone stopped. 'What is the meaning of this?'

Freddie looked at him. 'It's my birthday, sir.'

'Your birthday?'

'Yes, sir.'

'I see.' There followed a long pause, and then, 'I would like see you in my room,' he said. Without waiting for a reply, certain of being obeyed, he strode away.

Freddie stood up and grinned at the rest of the gang.

'Perhaps he's goin' to give you a present,' Ken said.

'More likely a thick ear,' Billie suggested.

Innocent of any crime, Freddie presented himself at the door of Mr Nicholson's office.

The man looked at him. His eyes held no warmth, no humour. 'Just what is the meaning of that...that uproar?'

Honest surprise looked out from Freddie's blue eyes. 'Matron said it would be alright. I bought the things with me own money, sir.'

94

'But it is NOT your birthday.'

'But, sir, it **is**.'

'This is September the fourteenth. Your birthday is on the eighteenth.'

'It...it can't be.' Freddie gaped at him. He'd always thought it was on the fourteenth.

'Don't contradict me. Do you think I'm an idiot? Do you think I haven't checked? Don't you think I know when your birthday is? You are a **liar**, Brayshay!'

'I...but I...me Dad sent the postal order.'

Tiny flicks of foam were appearing at the edges of the master's mouth. His face, his nose, even his eyes had turned red. 'I don't know what sort of a joke you think this is, but I am going to have to teach you that you can't get away with it here. Not while I'm in charge.'

As the cane once more seared his flesh Freddie tried to work out what had gone wrong. How he could have made such a mistake. He never found a satisfactory answer. He never again felt the same anticipation when his birthdays drew near. Nicholson had effectively ruined one more experience for life.

The bombing was now such that the safety of the boys evacuated to Fleetwood was questionable. Some people in authority began to murmur that they would all be better off at home with their own families.

Doubt and disquiet was reported in the local Fleetwood newspaper:

In the vulnerable areas the authorities are faced with an ever growing number of children running wild, without schooling, almost without control.

Places like Fleetwood are not happy at seeing their work going for nothing. They are less and less inclined to put up with the inconvenience of staggered school hours for their own children to bolster up a scheme they feel is failing.

Subdued, the boys waited to find out what would happen to them next. They knew they had no choices, no rights, they were like animals from a zoo being transported from one kind of imprisonment to the next.

For a moment a picture of Wolfgang Mozart came into Freddie's mind - the German Jew boy who had given him the running shoes. Somewhere he was locked away with hundreds of others just like him. At least in the Home they were not **that** badly off - at least he didn't think so.

Chapter 7

BAD TIMES - BROCKENHURST STREET

And then, for Fred, a miracle happened. First there was a letter he couldn't really make sense of, and a few days later John Airey arrived at the Old School House.

Mr Nicholson sent for him. His Dad was sitting on the edge of a chair in the 'dreaded study' looking anything but comfortable. Freddie stared at him. Although his father had visited him spasmodically since he came to Fleetwood, he hadn't noticed until now how much he had changed. His hair, which had receded even further from his forehead, was now almost grey. He seemed thinner than ever, and he looked so...so worn and old.

Then he lifted his head and smiled at Freddie with those piecing grey eyes that seemed to see and understand everything.

'Hello, Dad!'

'Freddie. How are you son? My, how you've grown!'

'I'm nearly thirteen now.'

'Yes, I know.'

Mr Nicholson cleared his throat. 'Your father has come to take you home.' He sounded annoyed, as if in some way it was a criticism of the way he ran things.

'Really, Dad?' Freddie couldn't believe his ears. So that's what the letter had been suggesting only he hadn't believed it. Hadn't dared to.

His father was nodding, smiling, holding out a carrier bag. 'Aye. Here's some clothes for you. Go along and change. You can't take away the clothes that belong to the Home.'

In the dormitory the other boys crowded around him. 'Aren't you comin' back?' Spider asked. 'Are you goin' home for ever? It'll not be the same with you gone.'

'You'll manage,' Freddie grinned. 'I've got to go now. Me Dad's waitin' for me.' He felt so wonderfully proud as he said those words. He wanted to run out of the building, to shout at the top of his voice, but if he broke any of the rules Nicholson might change his mind and prevent him from leaving.

He walked sedately back to join his father. In the hall he found him waiting. Mr Nicholson had disappeared. He didn't even stay to say goodbye.

Freddie kept asking questions. He still couldn't believe this was really happening to him.

'I've got a job back in engineering,' John Airey explained. 'We've only got a small house in Brockenhurst Street in Burnley, but it's a beginning. At least we'll be together.'

'What about her?' He couldn't bring himself to use the word 'mother'.

'Your Mam's got a job in a really smart shop. There's a restaurant over the shop there too. It belongs to Ralph Mason.'

He looked at Freddie thoughtfully. 'You'll be by yourself after school though until she finishes 'cause I work night shifts now. Do you think you can manage on your own?'

He laughed. Didn't his Dad know that in the Home they had to do everything for themselves? 'Oh, Dad! 'course I can.' he assured him joyfully.

When they finally arrived at Burnley railway station and climbed down on to the platform Freddie was shocked to see how dirty everything was. It hadn't been like that in Fleetwood, there everywhere was clean and fresh and the air from the sea had smelled different.

The house was another shock. Freddie knew the difference - even Long Row hadn't been like this. This was a real slum.

But there was no difficulty in adjusting to the outside world. After a few days it was as if his freedom had never been taken from him.

Now he went to Towneley Senior School and each afternoon when lessons were over he would return to Ralph Mason's restaurant in St James' Street. He could see his Mam loved working there. She still wore her make-up and red nail varnish, but she smiled a lot now, mostly for the benefit of the customers, especially the soldiers who came in to spend their money.

The staff in the shop and restaurant were very kind to him. They always had time for a word; occasionally he'd be given food they had failed to sell earlier in the week.

But still his mother did not come home. She promised, telling him to run on, that she'd be there soon.

The hours crept slowly past each evening as he waited in the street; cold and often wet through he would stare at the lighted windows where families - **real** families that he could picture in his mind - sat together listening to the radio, talking to each other, eating hot dinners.

For tuppence he could buy 'hot torpedoes' from the street vendors - meat and potato pies that only partially filled the hole inside his belly while he waited and waited.

Much later she would return home - this woman who was supposed to be his mother - reeking of alcohol, and he knew she had been at The Volunteer. Painfully he began to wonder if she was seeing other men while his father worked. He couldn't bring himself to tell his Dad. They rarely saw each other now in any case, for when his Dad returned from a twelve hour shift he was so tired he simply crashed out on the bed only rising in time once more to return to the factory.

Hungry and neglected Freddie roamed the streets, often missing school - no one cared anyhow. He would walk for miles and miles to visit the Clarkson family in Cliviger, knowing that there at least he would always be made welcome.

People in uniform, most of them strangers, walked about the streets smoking cigarettes; they smiled and spoke with strange foreign accents. Then there were the local people dressed up as ARP men who seemed to go around constantly shouting at everyone to 'put those lights out': there was the Auxiliary Fire Service and the women in uniform who went around looking proud and important, part of the Women's Voluntary Service.

The Government had asked for young men to volunteer to work in the mines but most chose the glamour of the fighting services. Eventually Ernest Bevan was forced to conscript young men by ballot into the pits. Forty five thousand, known as the Bevan Boys, went down the mines; they helped to bring out the coal so essential to the manufacture of iron castings and steel.

It was 1942. London was taking a real hammering. Everyone was talking about it. Hundreds of people made homeless from the bombing were appealing to the charity of relatives and friends to take them in and give them a temporary home.

Such a family arrived one day at Brockenhurst Street. They were Grace Mary's relatives - Mrs Touhey and her two children from Edmonton in London.

Gordon Touhey was about Fred's age. They ought to have been able to play together, to become friends. But Gordon was perfect - or so they kept telling Fred. The comparisons were continual and infuriating. Freddie's rating went from bad to worse. Angry, hurt, rejected, he spent more and more time away from the house. There wasn't even a bedroom for him to sleep in - THEY had it.

Someone finally realised there was a problem. Was it the school authorities? The welfare people? Or did his Dad at last see what was happening?

'You're quite poorly,' they told him, muttering something about TB and consumption. He'd lost far too much weight for a growing lad they said. At least they were worrying about him now it was too late. Freddie hoped he would die, that would teach them all a lesson. He wondered if they'd be sorry after.

'We're sending you away,' his Mam said. 'It's for your own good. I've discussed it with your father. You're to go to the Earnshaw's farm. The fresh country air will do you good.' She gave a funny little laugh. 'At least you won't have to eat dried eggs there or tinned milk powder.'

At the farm Mrs Earnshaw lead him into a little attic room with a view across the fields. It was clean and pretty.

'This is your room,' she told him. 'There's a cupboard for your things over there.' She pointed. 'Now we have to work hard on the farm. Up early every morning. But you're to take no notice. You just get up when you're ready. I shall leave your breakfast each morning in the kitchen.'

'Thank you.' He could hardly get the words out. A room to himself! With no Gordon Touhey or Mrs Touhey and no Mam yelling at him every time he put his head round the door. And everyone here was being so kind.

'We just want you to get well fast as you can,' she said.

It was like an absolutely perfect dream. Freddie was free to do exactly as he pleased. Sometimes he would lean on the rails of the sty watching the pigs. Other times he wandered into the fields where the men were working. He had heard that some farmers now used prisoners of war - one of the boys had told him that you could pick them out because they had to wear special clothing - but he never saw one.

More and more farms were becoming mechanised with farmers swopping horses for tractors whenever they had the chance, realising the importance of home produced food. Dig For Victory signs were plastered to bill boards. Ships that did attempt to get through with food from abroad were often torpedoed and hundreds of lives lost.

Freddie was fascinated by the farm machinery. He longed for the day when they would let him drive a tractor.

After years and years of rigid discipline his whole world had been turned around. Now, it seemed, he could do exactly as he wished. No one shouted at him, no one beat him, no one expected anything of him at all.

Gradually he began to feel stronger. His appetite was phenomenal. His energy returned and he longed to do things. Boredom began to set in.

The only thing causing aggravation in Freddie's life at this time was the huge white gander who lived on the farm and behaved like a watch-dog. Everyone was afraid of him. He would run hissing and snapping at bare legs, terrifying everyone indiscriminately into running the last few yards to the shelter of the building.

Perhaps it was pure unadulterated mischief in him, perhaps it was the gradual build up of energy that made Freddie one day decide to do something about the gander.

He was alone in the yard. On the far side he could see the great white bird rising to his feet, flapping his wings, psyching himself up for the attack.

Freddie bent down and grabbed a long stick from the ground. He lunged forward shouting at the gander. The bird, utterly confounded by this unexpected aggressive behaviour, turned and ran.

Yelling loudly Freddie went in pursuit. It felt wonderful to be out chasing this bird who had intimidated him for so long. Over the two acre field he ran - watching as the huge goose took off and flew down into Lydgate valley.

Finally he reached the village. Somewhere amongst the buildings the gander had disappeared. Breathless and elated Freddie stopped. He looked all around him, there was no sign, no sound of the bird. Triumphantly he began the long trek back to the farm singing happily to himself. It was a wonderful feeling just to be alive, to know that he had finally conquered his fear.

That evening he was sitting quietly reading a comic when Mr Earnshaw came into the parlour. He planted himself in front of Freddie. 'Where's my bloody goose?' he demanded.

Freddie looked up at him. There was no use denying it, he could see by the look in Mr Earnshaw's eyes that he knew the truth.

'I got rid of him for you,' Freddie said. 'He was always a nuisance. You said so yourself, lots of times.'

'That **nuisance**, as you call him, is our bloody Christmas dinner. So you can go back now and find him and bring him home.'

Freddie's eyes opened wide. How the hell was he supposed to make the gander come back? He didn't even know where he'd gone.

'You'll have to go with him, Jack,' Mrs Earnshaw said. 'If the bird has to run all the way back home there'll be no flesh left on him to eat.'

The wonderful sense of elation had evaporated. Freddie rose to his feet with sinking heart. Silently he climbed into Mr Earnshaw's old ford van.

'Have you seen a goose, please? A big white one?' He kept knocking on doors, asking, turning away as heads were shaken.

Finally he got a positive response. 'It's out the back,' a woman informed him. 'I guessed someone would be along sooner or later.'

'I'm the lad that chased him here. It...it was a kind of a joke,' he said feebly.

'Seems to me the joke's on you,' she said, smirking at his discomfort.

He followed her through the house and out into the back yard.

But the gander was both furious and afraid. He wouldn't let Freddie get anywhere near him. Mr Earnshaw was called in to assist.

He took off his jacket and dropped it over the bird's head and before it had time to do anything he neatly wrapped up the goose and tucked it under his arm. 'Thank you, missus,' he said. 'Sorry for the trouble.'

She stood there laughing as Freddie trailed after him.

'Get in. You'll have to have him on your lap.' Mr Earnshaw dumped the bird on Freddie's knees. 'An' don't you dare let go of him.'

Scene of the 'wild goose chase' - the bird finally disappeared amongst the houses seen in the distance

The next day Freddie was sent home. He had been away for just four weeks. The Earnshaw's must have decided that if he was well enough to run so far then he was well enough to return home and get on with his education.

Gordon's exemplary behaviour was thrust down his throat with even more vigour than before. Freddie hated the lot of them. **She** wasn't his real mother he kept reminding himself, she had never loved him, never wanted him.

By now he was convinced that the only reason they had him in the first place was because John Airey wanted a son. But he was never at home any more, he was always working.

Freddie made a decision - it was time to take things into his own hands. But he had to arrange them just right, for it was important that in order to accomplish his self-appointed task he must borrow his Dad's bicycle. This had to take place whilst his Dad was sleeping for he would need it the next evening to get to work. The way Fred saw it, so long as he returned the bike before his Dad needed it again no one would even notice it had gone.

In the early hours of the morning he crept from the house. The bicycle was an enormous old fashioned sit-up-n-beg type.

Freddie straddled the seat.

He looked around. Everything was quiet and still. There were no eyes watching from behind curtains as far as he could ascertain. For sure his Mam and the rest of them were still sleeping. Furtively he began to pedal away.

As he cycled along he became conscious that this was the first real wish he had ever had to escape from his family. He now looked upon them as people who had no right to him. He believed they no longer cared what happened to him and no one loved him. Determined to find his real mother and father he pressed on. They had to be **somewhere**.

The place to start, he decided, was at the orphanage in Leeds from where his Dad had once told him they'd fetched him as a little baby when he first went to live with them at Cliviger.

The journey from Burnley to Leeds was long and arduous. They had no maps at home that he could borrow and because of the threat of invasion all road signs had been removed. He was going to have to keep stopping and asking. Nothing was going to prevent him from reaching that orphanage and finding out what he wanted to know.

By ten o'clock he was feeling extremely hungry and thirsty. He stopped and pulled the few coins he had from his pocket. There was enough to buy a drink and a meat pie. He must go carefully though, he might need some money when he got to the city.

Inside the shop he stood waiting his turn, summing up the woman behind the counter. Dare he ask her the way to Leeds without arousing suspicion? Her face, round and soft, gave him confidence - a thin pinched face with narrow lips he had learned was to be approached with caution. Whatever happened, he didn't want her calling the police.

'Yes, sonny? What can I do for you?'

'A bottle of tizer and a meat pie, please.' He felt hot and conspicuous. Lifting his arm he wiped his sleeve across his forehead.

She pushed the goods towards him. 'You're lookin' a bit hot an' bothered,' she observed.

This was his cue. 'I'm on me way to Leeds. I have to meet someone there. I've been cycling all mornin'.' He hoped that sounded alright. Give her enough information to stop her asking questions but avoid the truth where there was a risk. 'I wondered if you could tell me the best way to go.'

She frowned, pursing her lips, concentrating. 'On yer bike you say?'

'Yes.'

'Well there is a bit of a short cut.' She stepped out from behind the counter and walked with him to the door; there she pointed out directions.

'It's still a tidy way,' she warned. 'All of twenty miles from here.'

'Thanks.'

He waited until she returned to the shop and then pedalled away balancing the drink and pie against his chest with one hand whilst with the other he controlled the steering.

Sitting on a bank a bit further up the road he ate his pie. He wouldn't ask for the orphanage he decided, not until he actually got into the city. He reckoned people there would be too busy to pay much attention to him.

The distance seemed interminable. He had, by this time, come to the conclusion that the bike was far too big for him, it seemed to weigh a ton. He stopped at the top of each hill to get his breath and look around. Several times he found it necessary to ask the way again. At least no one queried his right to be going there; as far as he could tell he had aroused no suspicion.

Noise and bustle heralded the city of Leeds. People and vehicles moved in a kaleidoscope of colour and activity. By the look of things folks here didn't seem to have much trouble with petrol rationing. There were rows and rows of red brick houses all looking exactly alike. It was much easier than Fred had imagined to move about un-noticed - a far cry from the inquisitive probing eyes of the people back home.

He propped the bike up against a lamp post and went into a shop. 'Do you know where the orphanage is?' he asked.

Uninterested they shook their heads. He might as well have asked the way to the moon.

At the post office he tried again. Surely they would know?

'What's it called?' For the first time someone really looked at him with an interest that had him worried. His mouth went suddenly dry and his tongue seemed to have swollen.

'I...I don't know the name,' he stammered. 'But it's here somewhere.'

'Perhaps it's been destroyed, or it might have changed its name. The army may even have taken it over. I'm afraid I can't help.'

Fred reached the door. No hand reached out to prevent him leaving. There was no police whistle, no shouting voices. He was safe, the man had already dismissed him and turned his attention to the next waiting person.

Several hours later Fred collapsed on a bench in a neglected park. The backs of his legs were burning and each time he moved his ankles red hot pains shot up his legs; his shoulders suddenly felt too heavy to carry around anymore.

A water fountain still stood on its stone pedestal. Hopefully he approached it and pressed the button. A clear jet of sparkling bubbles leapt into the air. Fred bent his head and sucked at it thirstily. He pushed his grimy face into the water gasping at the coldness. But it revived him, he began to feel better.

Picking up the abandoned bike he pushed it along in the gutter. He would try once more before giving up. He didn't know what else to do or where to go if he failed.

At The Briggate he leaned the bike against a wall. The thought came to him that somebody could easily steal it. Well, if they did he'd just never be able to go back home again. If his Dad didn't half-kill him his Mam would.

Suddenly he caught sight of his reflection in a plate glass window. He looked ridiculous. He had grown tall and so skinny his knee bones looked as if they belonged to an ancient horse. Grey woollen socks wrinkled his ankles. His fair hair stood up straight on the top of his head driven there by the wind. He was wearing a pair of his Dad's old trousers cut away to expose his awful legs. No wonder no one took him seriously when he asked the way.

But he must not give up. He approached a lady selling bunches of wild heather. 'Excuse me, do you know where the orphanage is?'

Uninterested in someone who had no intention of buying, she shook her head and returned to cry her wares.

Over and over again he asked: 'I'm looking for the old orphanage...do you happen to know where it is?'

Then, trying another approach he enquired, 'do you recall an orphanage that used to be here?'

Realisation came sadly, slowly to him. He was never going to find the place. The whole idea was hopeless. He must have been mad to think he could find out who his real parents were. Perhaps the orphanage didn't exist any more. Perhaps it never had.

Dejected, he dragged the bike away from the wall. If he could find his way out of the city he now knew he had no choice but to return home.

Fred lost count of the times he stopped, rubbing at his calf muscles, wriggling his shoulders and fingers to stimulate the circulation. He was going to be far too late to get back before his Dad missed the bike. Already it was dark and it looked as if it would start to rain at any minute.

Over the crest of the hill he dropped down into the valley. He could smell the wonderful smell of food drifting on the air. Hot food! It was the fish and chip shop in Cornholme.

Standing astride the bike he felt in his pockets. He still had enough money to buy a portion of chips.

Ten minutes later, tucking the steaming newspaper wrapped package inside his jacket, he gazed up into the hills where the Earnshaws' farm began. With a determined grunt he began pedalling towards it.

Reaching the long run of steps he dismounted and began to climb. Soft yellow light spilling out into the yard. He could even smell the paraffin fumes from the lamps. But the house was locked up for the night and there was no sound of voices.

Disconcerted, he hesitated. What would they say when they saw him? What would they think of him? The picture of himself as he had appeared in that shop window in Leeds came unbidden to his mind. He could not face them.

Silently he crept away.

At the dog's kennel he hesitated. He was cold, hungry and exhausted - and the kennel was empty. He crawled in through the opening. The straw had a definite doggie odour but it was warm and dry. He opened the newspaper and exposed his chips.

He awoke with the dawn, so stiff he could hardly move. Slowly he stretched letting out an involuntary cry as his feet hit the side of the kennel. With a start he recalled where he was.

He was unbelievably cold and hungry. An unknown feeling of utter desolation swept over him. Then his fingers touched the newspaper which had been wrapped around his chips. Inside, half the chips remained, congealed amongst the cold fat. He must, he realised, have been so tired the night before that he had fallen asleep without finishing them.

As he pushed the bike away from the farm he ate the cold chips and wondered what would happen when he arrived home.

It was no use. He couldn't bear to go back there. He thought of what his Mam would do to him, most likely with Gordon, the perfect boy, looking on. No, he would never go back. Never!

He made his plans as he rode towards Burnley. He was going to sneak the bike back home while no one was looking and then he was going to go away - so far away that no one would ever find him.

The first thing was to find somewhere he could spend the night. He thought of the bus station. At least there was a kind of shelter there.

When he knew for certain that the last bus for Barley had left, he made his way across the road and sank down on the bench seat in one corner of the shelter.

A man in overalls on his way to work paused,and looking down at Fred with a curious expression asked, 'What are you doin' 'ere?'

'I'm waitin' for the bus to Barley.'

The man shook his head. 'You've missed it, lad. The last one goes at eight o'clock.'

'Oh!' He tried to sound disappointed and surprised at the same time. 'When does the morning one go? I'll just 'ave to wait.'

The man sighed. 'You'd better come with me. If you've to wait till morning the least we can do is try an' give you a bit of comfort.'

He steered him round the corner to the Gas Works. Inside there was a bright coal fire burning in the iron grate.

The man pointed. 'Will that do you?'

The warmth was gentle, like summer in the middle of the night. Freddie moved closer to the flames. The heat intensified, soaking through his frozen bones.

'Here, get yerself round that.' The man gave him a sandwich and a mug of tea.

'I'll make you up somewhere so that you can lie down,' he said, pulling two chairs together and wrapping a blanket round Freddie's weary body.

It felt so good he didn't want to sleep. He just wanted to lie there for ever, safe and warm.

Despite his resolve, he was just drifting off into his dream world when the door opened. Sgt Millard stepped into the room and closed the door. Freddie sank down under the blanket.

'It won't do, Freddie. I can see you're there. We've bin lookin' everywhere for you.' The policeman approached the make-shift bed.

Freddie sat up. 'What you goin' to do with me?'

'Take you home. They've bin in a right state over you. When your Dad found his bike had bin brought back he reasoned you couldn't be far away.'

A look of fear cast shadows in his blue eyes. 'Please Mr Millard, don't make me go back. I can't bear it.'

'And why's that?'

'Me...Mam will lather me. They don't want me. She goes on at me all the time an' me Dad's never there, he's always workin'. I hate it there.'

'But you can't stay here, lad. They're responsible for you. Come along. I'll make sure your Mam leaves you alone.'

Freddie disentangled himself from the cover and stood up. His body still ached all over from his long struggle with the bike.

Slowly, painfully, he followed the policeman out of the Gas Works.

Sgt Millard opened the door of his car. 'Get in,' he said.

Miserable beyond words Fred hunched down in the seat; he was being taken back to that awful place where his Dad and Mam, with his Auntie and her two children all lived - the whole lot of them in two tiny bedrooms, a kitchen and a sitting room. As his Dad often said, there wasn't room to swing a cat around.

'Where've you been then?' the policeman asked.

'I went to Leeds.'

'That's a tidy way. What made you go so far?'

'I...I was lookin' for the orphanage.'

'I see. And did you find it?'

Freddie shook his head. 'I think it's not there anymore.'

'So where did you think to go next?' His voice was calm, reassuring, it welcomed confidences.

'I don't know. I just didn't want to go back there.' He pointed to the row of houses now stretching out in front of them.

'Don't worry about it any more.' Sgt Millard's voice had a steadying effect. 'It's goin' to be alright, lad. Don't you fret.'

Freddie watched as the policeman raised his hand and knocked on the old blistered paint work. Almost instantly his Mam's face appeared round the edge of the door.

'I've brought the lad back,' the policeman said. 'He's exhausted an' he's had as much as he can take for one day.'

'Oh, is that so!' Grace Mary stared at him with cold, unforgiving eyes.

'Aye, it is that, an' if you lay one finger on him... well, you'll have me to answer to, missus. Is that understood?'

Anger glittered in her eyes. 'Yes.' She spat the word at him.

'I'll be back tomorrow to see the lad's alright, so you'd better watch what you're doin'.

He turned to Freddie. 'You'll be alright now lad. Don't let them bully you.'

A long family discussion must have taken place after he had fallen asleep, it resulted in them unanimously agreeing he was unmanageable. The authorities intervening, probably at the request of Sgt Millard, decided he was in need of care and protection.

It wasn't possible for Freddie to return to St George's. He didn't know why they couldn't send him back, perhaps he was too old, perhaps they were full up. He wouldn't have minded too much going back there. He understood the regime - he was one of the boys, never singled out as he was at home for all the dirtiest jobs, the abuse and constant criticism.

Within days, without being given any option, he was taken to Buckley Hall in Rochdale. It was June 30th 1942.

Defenceless, he was thrust into an environment with youths convicted of every kind of crime. For the first time in his life he was in constant contact with villains and criminals.

Sick at heart and bewildered beyond any kind of understanding he waited to find out what would happen to him next.

Had they really put him here because he borrowed his Dad's bike? Because he'd slept at the Gas Works and lied about catching the bus? Was he really so bad?

Eventually someone did something for he was moved once more. He had been in the 'Home' for three weeks. It was to stay indelibly in his memory for the rest of his life. It was a violent environment that shocked and appalled him. Never in his whole experience had he encountered such people. Just being there was a punishment; everything had to be done on the double, the boys were constantly driven and yelled at by countless human beings all intent upon making their lives as miserable as possible.

If only he had known this was just a temporary measure - but no one told him anything - for Buckley Hall was a remand home owned by a Catholic Institution and Fred, quite definitely, was the responsibility of the Church of England Homes for children in need of care and protection.

Buckley Hall, as it is today. Photo taken from inside the 20ft high fence. By kind permission of the security guard.

Once more he was scooped up and carried off. This time to Standon Farm School in Standon Staffordshire. Freddie was thirteen years old.

The countryside looked the same. Stooks of corn stood about the fields like strange little girls in summer dresses waiting to go to a party. Some farmers could be seen still using shire horses, with huge white tasselled feet, to pull the carts, moving the produce from fields to farm yard. Fred had heard of strange foreign people from Ireland who had come to help with the crops but it was almost impossible for the local people to understand a word they spoke.

As the train thudded over the railway lines Freddie's attention was drawn to the towns and cities they passed through; whole blocks of buildings had been crushed to the ground as if a terrible giant had stamped angrily over the roof tops.

Some people said the war would soon be over, others said it would never end. It made no difference to Fred, like a cow bought at auction he was still ferried around as if he was nobody. He felt only idle curiosity at what the next place would be like - for sure it couldn't be worse than living at Brockenhurst Street or in the remand home in Rochdale.

He thought about the sad look in his Dad's eyes as he'd said goodbye. He guessed he still cared about him in a way, but the whole thing had got too much for him and with his Mam and Auntie going on and on - well, he didn't stand a chance. No wonder he buried his head in his bible and went so often to the new kind of chapel - anything must be better than being home with that lot.

At last the train stopped at Stafford. The welfare officer nudged him. 'This is where we get off.'

Fred lifted his bag. All he possessed in the world was contained within. Taking a deep breath he fell into step beside the person detailed to see that he arrived safely.

Chapter 8

BETTER TIMES - STANDON FARM SCHOOL

Outside the station a shining black Wolsey car stood waiting. The Welfare officer moved towards it. Fred stared in amazement. It couldn't be...it wasn't possible that he was being met by a car like this.

A man stood beside the car looking in his direction. He was a big man and the pork-pie trilby hat perched on top of his head made him appear even taller. The ginger moustache above his upper lip moved as he smiled. He reached out and Fred found himself shaking hands with the man who was to become everything to him for the next two years.

With a deep voice he heard him say: 'Hello, Fred. I'm Mr Dawson, your Headmaster.' Then immediately taking his leave of the welfare officer he opened the door of his beautiful black car. 'Come on lad,' he said. 'We've a long drive to Standon.'

The car interior smelled of leather. Fred sat looking at the fittings and upholstery, marvelling at it, wondering what had suddenly happened to his life that he should now be travelling, for the first time in his life, in such a car. What a difference to the old Sun bike his Dad used to have!

The very first thing that impressed Fred on his arrival at Standon Farm Industrial School was the welcome given to him by Mrs Dawson, matron of the school.

'Come along in,' she said. 'Tea's ready. Usually you'll take it with the other lads but on this occasion I thought you might like to have it with us. That way we can get to know each other and you can ask me anything you want to know.'

Note: There was no hint that Fred was there due to his alleged larceny which, in retrospect, he believes could only have been as a result of his mother's accusation following Fred taking his father's bicycle for the day when he went to Leeds.

Innocent of all this and of the label 'in need of care and protection', Freddie sank into the comfortable arm chair and sipped at the tea.

He eyed the two people sitting facing him with open curiosity.

He had expected someone like Mr Nicholson and a repetition of his first day at St

George's with the scrubbing he'd received in the merciless hands of matron - and that awful carbolic soap!

Mrs Dawson was so friendly. She explained that her job was that of matron in the school. 'I'm a kind of deputy mum,' she nodded, pleased with the idea. 'If you have any problems or you're not sure what to do or where things are - well, then you just come and find me.' Her lips parted and she gave him a lovely smile. 'I'll keep an eye on you, you'll be alright.'

'Thank you.' Freddie set the china tea cup down carefully on the table. He looked at these two people who were to be his guardians for the rest of his institutional days and he liked what he saw.

As he rose to leave the room Mrs Dawson gave him the times which were to rule his activities. All the boys rose at 6.30. Even before washing they were detailed to complete numerous chores including bed making and cleaning of dormitories. At 7.30 they washed and proceeded to the dining room for breakfast. At 9.0'clock they began their morning's work. 12.30 to 1.30 was set aside for dinner and more jobs. They then returned either to the classroom or to the workshop where they were being trained for eventual outside employment. At 5.30 they stopped for tea. After this there was recreation time followed by prayers and everyone had to be in bed with lights out by 8.30. On Saturdays, except for those who were involved in farming and milking, work ceased at 12.30.

The dining room, when he entered it, was so impressive that Fred stopped and stared: it was immaculate, with the floors so highly polished he could see the reflection of his own shoes in the waxed surface.

Each table seated five lads - two on each side and the fifth at one end. A sliding partition was designed to be pulled across the room when meal times were not in progress; this then acted as the recreation room for the inmates.

During that first meal with the rest of the boys Fred was introduced to some of the customs: crumbing was an organized activity which involved two boys, taking it in turns, to gather up any crumbs left on the table with moistened finger tips - the extra 'treat' was then hastily placed in the mouth and enjoyed with gusto whilst the rest of the eyes around the table looked on. It was immediately evident that food was not that plentiful and none was ever left or wasted.

Another unwritten rule was that one boy from each table carried back the empty plates. Fred's sides were to ache with laughter when, in the future, he would watch poor 'blob eyes' - who was usually unanimously elected to make the journey - struggle to cover the distance between table and kitchen without having a fit. The stress was often just too much for the poor lad, and as they watched him begin to shake and tremble the plates would fall from his hands and crash to the floor.

The cruelty of this was never apparent to them - in such circumstances they saw only that they had to make their own fun where they could and the unfortunate lad was seen as an opportunity for hilarity.

There were three dormitories inside the main building. Fred settled in amongst a group of boys with a feeling of security that had been missing from his life for a very long time. His eyes were alert to every new thing, his ears listened acutely to what the other boys said; this way he saw and heard in advance what life would be like and how to avoid the pitfalls.

Discipline was very prominent...and yet he sensed a kind of respect from the boys for the masters whose sole job was the moulding and building of their young lives.

Hopefully he wondered if he would be allowed to skip his last few months of schooling. But he was out of luck. On his second day at Standon Fred was taken by one of the older boys to the school room. Not very many boys in the Institution were young enough to still require formal education. The single room, quite separate to the rest of the building, was made of wood. Inside he discovered Mr Morrice, who would attempt, with whatever time was allotted him, to instruct Fred with a mixture of conventional learning. Here the boys were first placed for assessment and general instruction.

In the rest of the school Fred learned that the older boys were being taught skills and trades that would equip them for life. Many would eventually be shipped to Canada, America or Australia.

The majority of the building and its surrounding sixty acres was designed to give them initial training in various skills. There was the farming section where the boys kept cows, sheep and pigs; another department taught building skills including brick laying, painting and plastering; there was an enormous market garden which provided all the food for the sixty boys and staff of the 'home'; there was also a small elite group of boys trained in the fundamentals of electrical engineering.

And then there was the joinery division with its sawmill - Fred saw this as being the most enjoyable of the training available to him. He couldn't wait to get started. Here was something he really wanted to do very much.

On his fourteenth birthday he approached Mr Dawson. 'Sir, is there any reason why I can't start learning to do things like the older boys?' Quite frankly he was fed-up with what he saw as childish lessons. He wanted to **do** something that was useful.

Mr Dawson looked at him and slowly said, 'I've been thinking along the same lines myself. It's time for you to decide where you want to go in life. Is there anything you ever thought you'd like to do? Do you have any natural skills?' He was sitting in his study, elbows resting on his knees, leaning slightly forward, waiting for Fred's response.

'The only thing I'm any good at is drawin'. I won a competition at Holme school when I did a picture of the village, and I won another prize when I designed a Savings Poster while I was at Fleetwood.'

Mr Dawson sighed. 'I don't think you stand much chance of getting started in a career where you can use your artistic abilities. At least not until this war is over and the country is sorted out again. Is there nothing else you might like to have a go at, Fred?'

'I like machinery, cars an' things. And I think I'd like wood work.'

'Well, how about starting in the joinery section? We'll go and talk to Albert Foreman tomorrow. You couldn't do better than to put yourself in his hands for a couple of years, he is an excellent teacher,' Mr Dawson told him. 'Yes, Fred, I think that's the direction you ought to go.'

Rising, he placed his hand on Fred's shoulder. 'You're a cut above the rest,' he admitted. 'Most of them are never going to achieve anything. I want to see you make something of yourself, Fred.'

It was the first time anyone had suggested that being different was an advantage.

Fred began to experience the same kind of feelings for Mr Dawson he had once felt for John Airey. He wanted to please him. Within him, though unrecognised, there was also an unconscious need for approval.

With a sense of awe and excitement he began his training in the joiner's shop alongside some of the older lads.

The difference to him was incredible. All at once he began to feel as if he was somebody, that he could produce things that were both useful and beautiful.

To Fred's great joy the school had its own swimming pool and playing fields. His world was complete. After all those years of being pushed around he finally felt he had come home.

He discovered that in each training section one was graded according to one's ability, so that a boy would start as a Grade Four Tradesman, progress through to Grade Two, then Charge-hand and finally Foreman. Each boy received payment according to his grading and this money was put into a separate saving account until he needed it.

Pocket money was paid according to grades: Grade Four 1d. per week, Grade Three 3d. per week, Grade Two 6d. per week and Grade One 9d. per week.

The Instructors were solely responsible for the grading and conduct; behaviour and performance outside the trade departments was not taken into consideration.

Bonus money was also paid according to the Instructor's category of each boy as: Labourer at 4d. per week, Improver 8d. per week and Foreman 1s. per week.

114

After the money was given to the boys each Sunday evening they paid matron for their sweets and were then required to hand over the balance to the Headmaster who placed it in a bank account for each boy.

From Standon many of the boys were hired out to pick fresh fruit and vegetables. 'Eat all you like,' the farmer would say, pointing to the damson trees to be stripped.

It took less than twenty four hours for the lads to realise that his generosity was anything but kind. For those who over-indulged there were desperate frequent visits to the nearest toilet - or a race to the most convenient hedge. Thereafter they left the eating of damsons to newcomers and got on with the job of picking.

Unlike Fred's experiences with St George's Home, the money received from these labours was banked for them along with their other pocket money.

Everything was so orderly, and although the boys still did most of the jobs around the school - much as they had done in previous homes - here there was a full time cook, domestic help, a lady who saw to the laundry and sewing, and eight masters, who, apart from teaching during the day, were on a rota system after school hours to serve in a caring capacity.

Fred stood in the joinery shop watching the hands of Albert Foreman at work - he seemed more like an artist than carpenter sometimes. In one corner of the room he had gradually built a stock-pile of beautiful half inch oak panelling. He viewed anything less than this with disgust, refusing to believe that any imitations of the real thing would ever have a place in the world of woodwork, in furniture or house building. If the wood available to him for panelling was less than quarter cut he would turn away with a look of disgust - he would not contemplate using it.

Unaware of the privilege, Fred was being taught by a true craftsman.

There was great excitement amongst the boys and staff - plans to modernise and expand the school had just been approved; a new staircase was to be built connecting two separate parts of the school, modern washing facilities were to be added, and a 'quiet' and 'noisy' recreation room were to be made so that a greater choice of activities would be available.

Fred, along with all the other boys, was to be allowed to exercise his skills in helping with this enormous project.

Standon Farm School as it was in 1902 by kind permission of The Children's Society

Standon Farm School after the alterations and extensions with which Fred was involved

Recognising his competence in drawing, Mr Dawson gave Fred instructions to produce a picture showing the completed project for the school magazine which was to be sent to each of the 'old boys' from Standon. His pride in accomplishing this made him feel as if, at last, he had achieved something really important.

Between the boys and masters they built a row of communal showers and a brick extension to the building - they even made forty solid wood wardrobes for a girl's school owned and run somewhere else by the Church Charity.

Nearby, Fred discovered, was an enormous munitions factory known as Swynnerton. The women who worked there were accommodated in five hostels of a standard far above anything they had ever experienced in their own homes. The central social building was equipped with a theatre, cinema and gymnasium. Frequently the workers from the factory were entertained by top artists, and to the boys delight they were often invited and found themselves being included in the audience.

At other times the boys from the School (sometimes referred to as the Home) were singled out for special treats and would be invited to watch the latest films at the picture house. Coming back to relate the whole of the programme to those boys who had not, for whatever reason been included, elevated the teller to a position of total power. It was a heady experience and felt marvellous.

On Sundays, whenever it was possible, Fred would find an excuse to stay behind when the rest of the school went to church. Every boy was expected to sing in the choir and if one's voice didn't measure up to the required standard, then those boys were usually left behind to help in the kitchens. If you played your cards right you had the privilege of pumping the church organ - Fred, when he was forced to go to church, pumped the organ.

From where he sat behind the screen he could look out at the people, seeing them with their mouths opening and shutting like a lot of goldfish in a bowl. If he became too carried away and forgot to attend to the pumping of the bellows he would be brought severely to task by the perspiring organist struggling to maintain the rhythm of the hymn with insufficient air in the system; on those occasions a weird sucking wheezing noise could be heard coming from the innards of the instrument resulting in some of the congregation dissolving into titters and scarcely suppressed laughter.

In the recreation room the boys had acquired an old gramophone and some Victor Sylvester records. Holding a dining chair before them they would practice dancing to the beat of the music, hopeful for the day when Mr Dawson would allow the girls from a nearby school to attend dances held there. Often the sessions would end with the boys dissolving into heaps of laughter on the floor and the dancing lessons would degenerate into friendly wrestling and fighting.

There must have been part of Mr Dawson that longed to be in the fighting lines helping to win the war for he announced one day, to the amazement of all the boys, that he was going to form an army cadet corp. This meant that they would all be trained in how to fight and how to defend their country.

'We have no way of knowing how long this war will go on. Some of you are close to the age when you will be called up. This way you will be prepared and of some use when you have to go.'

Mr Dawson immediately gave himself the rank of captain; Mr Anslow and Mr Fieldhouse became one pip lieutenants.

Most of the boys heralded this new venture with enthusiasm - none more so than Fred. He loved the training, the discipline, the opportunity to prove himself.

The only cloud on his horizon was the conflict between his loyalty to the cadets and Mr Foreman his woodwork master. Almost from the beginning Mr Foreman had singled him out with an extraordinary kindness, and most week ends would actually take him home with him to spend two glorious days in a real home with all creature comforts, mothered by Albert Foreman's wife.

Now, with week ends away in training, he was rarely able to visit Albert Foreman's home. At first there was a strange distant atmosphere between Fred and the master that he could not define - almost as if Mr Foreman resented him going with the cadets. On several occasions it erupted into open anger.

Truly believing in what he was doing Fred stood up to the master. Why had he turned against him when he became a cadet? Gradually he came to realise that Mr Foreman had very strong feelings about the whole organization - whether he was in reality a conscientious objector or just felt it wrong for the boys to be trained in fighting Fred never found out. It made him sad but there was nothing he could do about it.

Very soon he found himself being promoted to Lance Corporal. He wore his uniform with pride, never minding the hours required to keep it looking so smart, his boots black and shining, his belt blanco'd to a dazzling white.

From somewhere Mr Dawson even managed to obtain weapons for them to practice with - suddenly they were no longer boys, they had become men.

Divided into two platoons they were attached to the local Royal Artillery. Being cadets also meant attending week-end camps at Park Hall, Oswestry, Shropshire.

At the Home they spent weeks studying and memorising the black outline shapes of the German planes. For hours they watched films depicting the planes in flight along with the engine sounds: in just a few short weeks they had become experts in the art of aircraft recognition.

Eventually all those boys involved passed the required tests and were attached to the local Royal Observer Corp.

On nights never to be forgotten Fred found himself with the Royal Observers, out all night with binoculars searching the skies for enemy planes. He saw these men - too old to enlist - as a group of right old codgers who needed the keen eyesight of the younger men and boys to compensate for their own, often failing senses. Mixing up the sounds of the engines, incorrectly identifying enemy planes with their own would have lead to disaster.

Fred was always hoping to see a Stuka. He remembered using that particular aeroplane in the National Savings poster he had painted - the one that had won him first prize. There were Heinkels, Messerschmitts and Dorniers to look out for, but it was always a Stuka he longed to spot.

The fact that they rarely saw or heard anything did nothing to detract from the excitement - the exhilarating sense of expectancy was always there; the thought that perhaps, one day, they would do something that would help to win the war.

Sadly, their importance to the war effort was considerably diminished as they only went on duty at night when they could rarely see any planes anyway and they were never quite certain as to which engine sounds were those of the enemy and which were their 'own'.

To the boys those times under canvas were fantastic. For whole weeks, under the supervision of Charlie Bartram, acting commander of the battalion, Fred acted as Regional Sergeant Major to the whole group of cadets from North Staffordshire who were in camp.

Without a doubt that first occasion in August 1943 was the most important in Fred's young life. Fifteen years of age, trained and moulded by Dawson and his staff for the last year, he was about to assemble the cadet force battalion from all over Staffordshire on the parade ground at Shrugborough Park.

Captain Dawson and second lieutenant Bill Fieldhouse spent at least an hour with Fred preparing him for this mammoth task.

Finally they watched as Fred drilled the battalion, knowing that from all the Companies the Commander had chosen their Sgt Major to act as R.S.M. for the period they were to be in camp.

'Battalion - Battalion Shun'. At least two hundred cadets responded to Fred's crisp command as he reported to the C.O. that the battalion was all present and correct.

But custard and corned beef, served up by the American cooks, mixed and eaten together was something else! The boys pulled faces at each other and then grinned - after all there was a war on and they didn't want to be thought soft - if the Americans could eat it then so could they. Sitting around in the tent they dug into the strange food, which, under the circumstances tasted remarkably good.

Nelson Hall, the local hostel, had been taken over by the Americans. After they had participated in so many raids over enemy territory they were being sent there to recuperate. The Americans, far from home, adopted the school wholeheartedly, and food, such as they had never seen before, began to appear on the boy's plates.

The Master Sergeant saw to it that they lacked for nothing. That Christmas was the best they had ever experienced.

It was 3.30 on a Friday afternoon and Fred was helping Mr Foreman to complete the 'glueing-up' of the ash wardrobes they had made for a girl's school near Stafford when the door suddenly opened and Mr Dawson, who was rarely seen in the workshops, stood there looking in at them.

He did not enter but beckoned to the master.

Mr Foreman addressed Fred: 'Carry on, Brayshay. I will be back soon. Garnett, you can help him finish off.'

This was such an extraordinary happening that the boys immediately stopped work and gathered round the small window overlooking the quadrangle of the main school building.

West said, 'I wonder what's up? It's not often old Dawson comes over here during the day.'

Very soon it became evident that something very serious was going on as they watched the masters, Morrice, Anslow, Wharton and Astley rushing towards the office situated in the corner by the kitchens.

The boys speculated as to the reason for the hasty gathering of the masters.

'I'll bet the war's over,' said James.

But no one appeared overjoyed, in fact the very expression on the faces of the men filled the boy's hearts with a kind of awe.

'Perhaps it's something to do with food poisoning,' another lad suggested. 'I saw a van this morning. It had Ministry of Food written on the side of it. That's what it is.'

Fred moved from the window. 'Come on you lot, let's get this job finished.'

Reluctantly they all returned to their respective benches and half-heartedly continued with their jobs.

Fred and Garnett had just completed the final wardrobe when there was a loud knock at the door. The girl from the office walked in and, pointing a finger at Fred, she motioned for him to step outside.

'Look Brayshay,' she said. 'Mrs Dawson wants to see you straight away in her lounge. Come with me.'

Fred followed. He was in no way afraid of Mrs Dawson. She was a lovely caring person respected by all the boys and Fred had often thought how he would have liked to have her for a mother.

It was, he realised, probably only the third time that he had been in this room: first when he had arrived, the second occasion when he had been promoted to Sergeant Major in the army cadets, and now. The other times had been all important mile stones in his life. What could it be this time?

Olive Dawson began at once. 'Now Fred, you must have seen all the activity going on during the last hour...' For a moment she paused, and then continued, 'The trouble is that Mr Dawson is very upset because one of the rifles is missing from the armoury. As you are the sergeant major, can you remember putting them all back after drill last night?'

For a moment Fred felt a chill of fear, aware of the enormous responsibility that rested on him alone. Then he replied firmly, 'They were all put back at eight o'clock and the door was locked. Well, at least it was closed against the yale lock.'

Mrs Dawson left the room. Fred stood silent, waiting, a thousand thoughts whirling through his mind.

When she returned she addressed him once more in her calm manner. 'Right, Fred. You can go back now but I want you to promise me that you won't say anything about this to anyone.'

Fred nodded. 'Okay, Mrs Dawson.' He didn't need to be told the seriousness of what had happened.

Slowly he made his way across the yard knowing full well that there were many pairs of eyes watching him, eagerly waiting for any giveaway signs that would indicate whether it was a good or bad situation that existed.

As he approached the joiner's shop Fred shook his fist at the faces in the window and by the time he entered the room the boys were back at their benches hard at work.

'What's up, Fred?' Immediately they crowded around. 'What's happened? Why have the masters gone to the office?'

Words were hurled at him in all directions. Fred realised the impossible position that Mrs Dawson had placed him in. What could he tell the boys? How could he explain the reason for him being called to see Mrs Dawson?

He decided to say nothing. Mr Foreman would be back soon. They would have to wait.

A moment later the door to the joiner's shop flew back against the wall as Albert Foreman kicked his way into the room.

His face was a picture of anger, resentment and unleashed frustration. 'Bloody army cadets! I knew that there would be trouble sooner or later.'

He whacked Fred around the head. 'You buggers, you should be more careful with the guns.' He thumped his fist down on the bench. 'Everybody is under suspicion now. I can't go home this weekend unless that bloody rifle is found.'

Fred was relieved that he had managed to keep silent. He had always known that Mr Foreman and one or two of the other masters were totally opposed to the formation of the army cadets. This incident, he realised, could well result in the whole unit being disbanded.

When Mr Foreman had calmed down he said: 'You are all to assemble in the recreation room at five thirty before tea.'

The boys came from every direction having completed a full day's work at bricklaying, painting, woodwork, gardening, farming or electrical work.

As they made their way to the recreation room there was an air of anticipation and excitement rippling through the group brought about by this change in normal procedure.

The room was large and easily accommodated all the boys; they sat against the walls in numerical order from one to sixty.

Mr Fieldhouse, the gardening master, told the boys to settle down and then to 'number off' to ensure that everyone was present.

Used to being known by numbers, and to break with the monotony of routine, they often changed their voices when responding. But on this occasion there was nothing further from their minds than turning the assembly into one of hilarity or fun.

Grace started off: 'One' he called out.

Shepperd followed. 'Two.'

They reached thirty eight when a silence fell. There was an empty chair. Everyone looked at it.

'Has anyone seen Cooper?' Mr Fieldhouse asked. His expression was stern, accusing.

The boys all knew that Cooper was a sickly lad who was constantly in and out of the Sick Bay; he was the sort of boy who would be least missed.

Mr Dawson entered the room followed by the total staff of the Home including the sewing lady, cook and office girl.

The silence was broken by Mr Fieldhouse whispering to the Head that every boy was present except Cooper.

Mr Dawson turned on Mr Morrice the assistant master. 'You must have missed

Cooper this morning. He's in your class.'

Morrice shook his head. 'No, sir, I didn't. But that can be explained. You know we are very overcrowded in the school room, one missing can easily go undetected.'

Dawson grunted. Fred watched closely, knowing that Dawson was not too keen on Morrice and had very little respect for him as a teacher.

Straightening himself to a height of over six foot the Headmaster cleared his throat. 'I called this special assembly because one of the .22 Canadian rifles is missing from the armoury and no one leaves the premises until it is found.'

He glared at them accusingly. 'We will search every inch of the school including the fields until it's found.'

Mrs Dawson turned to her husband. 'But, Tom! What about Cooper? Isn't it possible that he could have taken the gun and run away?'

The Headmaster looked all around the room, eyeing each boy individually and then turned to the staff for their reaction. The negative response only went to confirm his own belief that Cooper, timid and pathetic, would not have had the gumption to carry out the theft.

He looked at his wife, doubt written on his face. 'I don't think so, Olive,' he said.

A missing rifle was not to be taken lightly. All of the boys were aware of the seriousness of the offence. But the possibility of a boy absconding, was to them a routine matter, for it happened on a regular basis. Their guess, unspoken, was that Cooper had simply run away.

The search for the rifle was organised by Bert Anslow, who, apart from being the electrical teacher was also a one pip officer in the cadets.

Watching and listening, Fred wondered whether this was Mr Dawson's way of putting Anslow to the test.

'Brayshay.' Fred looked directly at the master.

He said, 'First thing tomorrow you and the joiners will cover all the outbuildings including the old gym. Linacre, you and the building boys will search the main school.'

The boys began to move towards the door. 'And I,' he concluded, 'will direct the rest of the boys in searching all the grounds. Good luck!'

The following morning they began the search. Normally the Saturday morning would have been devoted to cleaning and maintenance of the school. To the boys it was a terrific change as they set off enthusiastically to investigate the outbuildings.

They made their way round starting from the old gym, the toilet block, the sewing room and laundry - up to the joiner's shop where they could hear a banging noise coming from the far end.

Inside they found Mr Foreman working. He glared at them and then addressed Fred: 'What do you want?'

He was astounded at the master's resentment. 'We are searching for the rifle, sir.'

Reluctantly he allowed them to make their search - opening cupboards, openly investigating his office, turning out boxes and peering beneath piles of wood - but they found nothing.

Leaving the workshop the boys went in search of the rifle in the remaining outbuildings. Again they found nothing.

Disappointed, they made their way back to the recreation room to report to Mr Anslow.

The field search had also proved negative and Anslow was already there waiting for the others to return. Now it only remained for Linacre and his group to arrive from their search of the main building.

The dining room had been kept open to feed the boys and staff during the day and it was about five thirty when the boys from the building department washed and went in to eat a well-earned tea.

Ron Linacre, one of the senior boys, known as a bully, spoke for the group. 'Well, that's it,' he announced. 'Nothing doin'. We've been through the whole place.'

Bert Anslow shrugged his shoulders and told the boys to assemble in the recreation room ready for bath night; this always took place on a Saturday night accompanied by a complete change of clothing for all the boys.

The routine was a simple one; the boys were given clean underwear, shirts, shorts and socks and were sent downstairs in groups of twelve to the ablutions block.

Fred, whose number was 35, went with the third group. As they descended the stairs and marched along the corridor by the dining room he reflected on the day: I wonder where old Dawson is? I haven't seen him around. I suppose he's been out with the villagers looking for Cooper.

Arriving at the locker room they encountered the previous group of lads collecting their dirty clothes from the lockers to take them upstairs. There they would be inspected by the master on duty to ensure that no filthy pants were sent to the laundry.

Fred's group were told to stand still.

'Shut up!' Mr Barby suddenly shouted.

Surprised by his tone their voices faded.

'What was that noise?' he asked.

It sounded like a voice from the other side of the ceiling.

The boys froze. 'Look, the trap door's not closed,' the master said. 'Go and get a pair of steps, Brayshay.'

Fred dashed away, returning a few minutes later with the steps. He set them up beneath the trap door and watched as Barby, who was partially disabled, ascended with obvious difficulty.

With heads tilted they observed his progress as he eased himself through the opening; then, in the space above them they saw a light go on.

'Oh, my God!' gasped the man. And then, 'Brayshay, come up here.'

Fred followed anxiously, dreading and fearing whatever it was that had caused the master's cry.

As his eyes became accustomed to the lesser light, he saw at the back of the party wall which separated the locker rooms from the bathroom a pitiful figure slumped against the roof strut.

'I think it's Cooper, sir,' Fred said. 'Look, he moved.'

They climbed along the ceiling joists and quickly confirmed that is was the poor lad.

Whimpering softly he cried out, 'I don't want to live no more. I tried to do away with meself.'

They saw that he had crudely tied a lanyard around his neck and had attempted to fasten it to a rafter.

Tired cold and hungry he had given up.

Lying across his legs was the gleaming form of the 0.22 rifle. Cooper's left hand rested on the butt.

'Disarm him but be careful!' Mr Barby instructed Fred.

But as Fred approached the boy he felt quite certain the gun was empty. The bullets, he knew, were always kept in the cupboard in Mr Dawson's office. Quietly he bent down and recovered the rifle.

Several more boys were then called up into the loft. Half-carrying, half-dragging him, they manoeuvred the boy to the opening.

Somehow between them they lowered him down into the waiting arms of the boys below.

Silent and subdued they carried him to the Sick Bay.

The following day he was taken away and was never seen again at Standon.

Note: No one was ever to forget the impact this incident had on the school or the inmates. Part of the 1947 Home Office report following the revolt and murder of a master (details of which are given at the end of this book) which relate to this incident are disputed by Fred who is adamant that it took place on the Friday and Saturday and NOT the Sunday as stated. The delay in reporting this may have been due to the fact that they were hoping to discover the missing rifle without having to report its loss.

Fred was fifteen when he discovered that Mr Dawson, with the help of Charlie Bartram, Captain of the Stafford cadets, had been pulling strings to get him started in an apprenticeship. Despite many war jobs being available, indentured apprenticeships were scarce, too many skilled men were either still away or had been killed - and so it was with a great sense of achievement that Mr Dawson informed Fred that they had arranged for him to have an interview with the Lotus Shoe Company.

Mrs Dawson had seen to it that he had some decent clothes to wear for the occasion. As they journeyed towards the factory Fred sat silently beside Mr Dawson wondering what questions they would ask him. He hoped he wouldn't let him down. The trees swished past, heavy with their unshed red and golden leaves.

The training he was offered filled Fred's heart with hope. He was to get a grounding in using all the woodworking machinery and he would be taught the basics in woodcraft and joinery.

'You will, of course, be expected to provide all your own wood-working tools,' the personnel officer told him.

Fred looked at Mr Dawson. This was something he had not even considered. But his Headmaster was nodding as if it was the most natural thing in the world. 'That will be no problem,' he said. 'Fred will bring his tools with him.'

One evening, shortly after the interview, Mr Dawson came to find Fred. 'I want you up early tomorrow,' he said. 'We're going to Birmingham.'

Fred looked at him in surprise. He sensed a controlled excitement in his Master and knew something was afoot.

'May I ask what for, sir?'

Dawson hesitated for a moment and then replied, 'You need tools before you start your job, don't you?'

'Yes, sir.'

'Right. Tomorrow we are off to the city to select them.'

Fred didn't know how he managed to sleep that night. Mr Dawson was taking him out for the day - just the two of them - and they were going to a special place to choose the tools he would need for his apprenticeship. He tried to visualise the day and the tools they would buy. How much would it all cost? Would Mr Dawson let him decide for himself or would the whole transaction take part without him being included?

He woke at dawn. Turning in his bed he looked at the watch John Airey had given him so many years ago. It was not quite six o'clock. If he got up now he'd still have and hour to wait before breakfast. He turned in his bed, pulling the covers up over his head, shutting out the light.

But it was no use, his mind refused to be still, he kept trying to picture the city and the showroom they were to visit. It was like waking to a very important birthday.

Abandoning the idea of sleep he slipped quietly from his bed and dressed. Trying hard to make no sound he tip-toed down the corridor. As he approached the kitchens he could hear someone already moving about.

Cautiously he opened the door. Mr Dawson was already there cutting rashers from a side of bacon. He smiled at Fred. 'So you couldn't sleep either,' he said.

Sheepishly Fred grinned back.

'Let's have a good breakfast and then we'll get started,' Mr Dawson said, and suddenly Fred understood, this was a special day for him too - it wasn't often, if ever, that Mr Dawson involved himself in such an expedition. He could, of course, have sent the woodwork master - instead he had chosen to take Fred himself.

He'd never understand why Mr Dawson was so kind to him but he would be forever grateful.

The centre of Birmingham was still shrouded in mist. Beautifully carved and decorated brewer's drays pulled by plodding horses moved over cobbled streets. Men with hand carts carrying fruit and vegetables brightened the scene.

'This is it,' announced Mr Dawson, turning into a yard and stopping the car.

Tilting his head, Fred read the sign hanging over the door. Parker Winder & Achurch, manufacturers and suppliers of tools.

Following Mr Dawson closely they went inside.

The collection of tools on display was so impressive that Fred feared he would never be able to make the right choices. But Mr Foreman had already spoken with the Headmaster and he appeared to know exactly what Fred would need.

The sales man was most helpful. 'Now you'll be wanting saws.' He reached into a cupboard. 'One cross-cut and one panel saw.' The man placed several on the counter.

'Which are the best?' Mr Dawson asked and didn't bat an eyelid when he heard the price.

'Take a hold of it,' the man said to Fred. 'It has to feel right. It must fit better than a glove. It's going to become like an extension of your own arm.'

As Fred held the saw, feeling the weight and balance of it, looking down at the silver metal teeth which had never yet eaten into a piece of timber, he noticed the brass plate screwed to the frame: *Manufactured by Henry Disston, USA.* It seemed incredible that all this way across the Atlantic they were selling tools made in America. Beneath the name was engraved in clear scrolled letters something that pleased and surprised him even more: *For beauty, finish and utility this saw cannot be excelled.*

Eyes shining, he looked at the two men who awaited his verdict with amused tolerance, as if they had all the time in the world while he, just a lad, made his decision.

'This is it. I'd like this one.' From the moment he took the saw in his hand he had known it was the one for him.

They went on to choose chisels, a full set of Marples firmer chisels and one set of bevel edged.

'Now what about planes?' Mr Dawson was addressing the man.

Fred began to feel as if his eyes would pop right out of his head as the planes were spread before him.

An hour later, with a Stanley jack plane and a smoothing plane added to his selection, he watched as they were made into two parcels.

Mr Dawson offered to help carry them out to the car, but he refused politely. They were his and he must get used to carrying them. As soon as he got back to Standon he was going to make the best tool box anyone had ever seen in which to keep them.

By the time they left the showroom the morning was already well on its way. Together they walked the wide open streets until they found a restaurant that satisfied Mr Dawson's expectations. 'Right, Fred. All this excitement has made you hungry I'll be bound. Let's go and eat.'

You had to have been a boy who had been pushed around, put in and taken out of homes, rejected by your adoptive parents, labelled as a menace disruptive and unmanageable, to understand how he felt sitting there calmly eating dinner with this great man.

Afterwards, when the others asked him, he hadn't the slightest idea what he had eaten and he didn't know where to begin to describe the marvellous feelings of the day which still remained, stored away forever, to be taken out in the future whenever he felt low, and like precious gems viewed and reviewed growing ever more glowing and valuable with the passing of time.

'This job means rising really early each morning,' Mr Dawson told him as they walked back to the car. 'But I'll get up with you to make sure you have a decent breakfast before you leave. Lotus is a good company, I don't want you to lose this opportunity by being late and missing your train in the mornings.'

As good as his word, for the rest of the time Fred stayed at Standon Farm Industrial School Mr Dawson rose each morning at six o'clock and cooked Fred a hearty breakfast before seeing him off on his way to Standon station from where he made the fourteen mile journey to Stafford. Then, putting his feet firmly one in front of the other he walked the last two miles to the factory.

The joiners in the workshop were good to him. He supposed, because of his training in the Home, he'd learned to get on with things without whining. He wanted to complete his training without a blot on his copy-book. Having been given this chance he wasn't going to let Mr Dawson down.

Fred's time in the home was coming to an end. Reluctantly he agreed to go into digs. 'We won't lose touch with you Fred,' Mr Dawson told him. 'This is still your home and you can come and see us whenever you want.'

It was with difficulty that accommodation was found for him with a middle-aged couple in the village of Burton Manor. The rent was thirty shillings a week. As his wage at that time was twenty eight shillings the extra two required was to be provided by the School; Mr Dawson, somehow aware of his needs, contributed an extra five shillings as pocket money for Fred.

THE CHURCH OF ~~E~ ~~ENGLAND WAIFS~~ & STRAYS SOCIETY

Secretary :—
Mr. W. R. Vaughan.
Headquarters :—Old Town Hall, Kennington, London, S.E. 11.

Notice of Discharge. BOY.

IMPORTANT : *This form should be filled in and sent to Headquarters immediately a child leaves the Home.*

HOME__Standon Farm School, Standon, Stafford.__

NAME___Frederick BRAYSHAY.__

AGE___16 yrs. 3 mths.___ Date Confirmed __August 1st 1943.__

Date Discharged___8th January, 1945.___

EMPLOYMENT (*If placed in situation.*)

Name of Employer_____Messrs Lotus Ltd.,_____

Address_____Stafford._____

1. Is the Employer a member of the Church of England ?_____

2. Is the Employer known personally to any member of
   the Local Committee or supporter of the Society ?_____

3. Have you or any member of the Home Committee seen
   the Employer or place of Employment ? ___*Yes.*___

4. What wages will the boy receive ?___*28/- p.w.*___ 5. With or without Board ?_*Without.*_

6. What arrangements have been made for Pocket
   money, Clothing and Washing ? ___*Lodgings have yet to be found.*___

7. What will be the nature and hours of the Employment ? *7.45 am. to 5.0 pm. Cabinet maker.*

8. What prospects are offered by Employer ? *Full Training in Building Dept. Office + shops.*

9. Has the boy been commended to the care of local Clergy ?___*No.*___

10. Does the boy wish to be enrolled as a member of 'OUR BOYS LEAGUE' ?_____

11. Has Employer been notified of National
    Health Insurance requirements ? ___*Yes.*___

12. What is the cost of outfit supplied to the boy ? ___*£9. 0.0. + Kit of tools.*___

13. How much has boy to refund and by what instalments ? (*See note.*) *None.*

14. Has boy been immunised against diphtheria,
    if so, how has certificate been disposed of ? ___Yes - no certificate.___

(*Signed*)_____*T. Dawson.*_____

N.B. In P.A.C. cases please send with this form details of outfit supplied, showing cost of each item
The boy should not be asked to refund anything.

*The discharge paper from Standon Farm School which set Fred free. Received by Fred on
13 September 1991 from The Children's Society in London*

No suitable lodgings have not been obtained for the lad. He is at present living at the School & travelling to Stafford each day.

When lodgings have been found, we shall have to augment his wages, but until these have been decided on the amount to be supplemented each week cannot be stated.

For the first week of course he has received no wages. He will only have 2 or 3 days to take next week.

At present, the School is paying travelling and mid day meal at the Canteen. 3/6 p.w. travelling & 2/6 p. week. meals.

This boy is being given a very fine chance to learn a very good trade. Cabinet making & Shop fitting. They for have their own drawing office and the boy is to spend part time in the office & part time in the shops. This first week he has spent showing what he is capable of doing and I think has proved himself.

T Dawson

Internal note written by T Dawson, Headmaster of Standon Farm School, to Mr W R Vaughan secretary of The Church of England Waifs and Strays Society. Received 13 September 1991

Truly independent at last, with money of his own to spend, Fred began cautiously to expand his world - although, in truth, there was little time left for anything when he finished at the end of each day for the Dodd's house was a long way from the shoe factory.

May 7th 1945

Finally, as if everyone had become too weary to carry on any longer, the war with Germany drew to a close.

The official celebrations took place on May 13th. For two days almost everyone stopped work while dancing, singing and drinking continued right through the night;

people went almost crazy as they came to terms with the reality that the long terrible war was over.

For the children there were races to be run in the streets, and trestle tables - dragged out from schools and village halls - groaned beneath the food contributed by people who had stored and saved it for so long. (They had yet to discover that rationing was to continue and that it would be years before many kinds of foods, familiar before the war, returned to the shops).

After more than 2,000 nights of black-out the lights were turned back on. This afforded Fred a new freedom, and determined to control his own destiny, he acquired a bicycle. Now, when he chose, he could visit Standon School after work or at week-ends.

On August the 14th Japan finally surrendered unconditionally to the Allies. This time celebrations of any kind were subdued, for with victory came also the knowledge of the horrors of the atomic bomb. It left everyone shaken and appalled by what man was capable of doing. In total the war had claimed over 55 million lives.

In the autumn of 1946, Fred went back to Standon to talk to Mr Dawson.

'I want to go and do my bit in the army,' he announced.

Dawson's eyes twinkled. 'It's not going to be like the camps you attended as a cadet, you know. Although the war is over there's still a terrible mess to be cleared up and sorted out. The whole world's in chaos. Why don't you have a word with Mr Hall, your manager at Lotus, he may be able to get your national service deferred until you have completed your apprenticeship.'

'But I **want** to go **now**, sir. It won't be the same if I wait another two years.'

Deep understanding linked the older man with the young one. 'You can't wait to get involved in what you think is going to be fun,' he stated.

'It's not that, sir. I know Lotus'll keep my job open for me. I can come back and finish my apprenticeship.'

'Then there isn't much else for me to say, except do your best, Fred. But then I know you won't let the School down.'

They shook hands, reminding Fred for a moment of that first time when he'd seen Dawson waiting beside the shiny black Wolsey outside Stafford Railway station back in 1942.

'I'll go and find Mrs Dawson now and say cheerio. And thank you, sir. Thank you for everything. I'll never forget what you've done for me. Coming to Standon was the best thing that ever happened to me.'

Two months later Fred joined the army. Almost before he knew what was happening he had completed his initial training and by 1947 was in Malaya. As the troops struggled with a strange environment, a foreign language, coping away from all home comforts, Fred found himself for the first time in his life appreciating the harsh training of his former years. Through all that had happened Fred Brayshay had learned, not only how to survive but how to excel in what he was called upon to do.

In 1948 Fred, having acquired the rank of sergeant, left the army and returned to Stafford to complete his apprenticeship with the Lotus Shoe Company.

Eventually he left Stafford in 1953 and began to travel the country in his new capacity as a qualified carpenter and joiner - once more living in digs.

Fred aged 21 years
in Blackpool
having just completed
his service in Malaya

Chapter 9

A LIFE OF HIS OWN

Fred and Pam at Hammersmith Palais where they met

March 29th 1958

Fred looked at his new wife. Standing before him wearing high heeled shoes she was of almost equal height. 'Sure you don't want to change your mind?' he said quietly.

Her bright eyes, wide and sparkling, held his gaze. She smiled, leaning forward to kiss him. 'Come on,' she said. 'The guests are waiting.'

Although he enjoyed the following hours, the fun, the celebrations, the wonderful feeling that everyone wished them well, it wasn't until they finally escaped and were driving away to begin their honeymoon that he really felt he was married. For the rest of their days together he was going to be happy. What's more he was going to do everything within his power to make sure Pam was too and that she never regretted today.

'How's it feel to be married?' he asked.

'Oh Fred!' she sighed. 'I can't really believe it's happened. I never thought my Dad would ever allow it.'

A constable in the Metropolitan Police, rigid in his discipline, scaring off any would-be suitors, he'd sometimes half-scared Fred to death, though he would never have admitted it. But he had been determined, from the first time he saw her, that one day he would marry Pam, and nothing and nobody was going to stop him.

'You're quite happy to be touring around for your honeymoon?' he asked.

It had been his idea. He'd met all Pam's family, but there hadn't been anyone of his own at the wedding, not a single relative. Now at least he could show her where he'd grown up. Most of all he wanted to see if he could find John Airey, he wanted very much to walk in and show off his new wife.

On the way to Blackpool they stopped off at Burnley. Without any difficulty they located 28 Kinross Street, the last address he had where he might locate his father. It looked like a typical council house with a sad hopeless neglected air about it.

To Fred's dismay he found John Airey in bed; frail, pitifully thin, unable to speak. His grey eyes, once so alert and piercing, appeared now even more deeply sunken into the bone framework of his face; once alive with ideas and vitality those same eyes now looked out at him, an echo of the man.

For several minutes they stared at each other. Then, using a pad of paper and a biro pen John Airey slowly scrawled: **THIS IS MY SECOND STROKE.**

Fred swallowed. 'I'm sorry. Is there anything I can do?' He wanted to comfort him, to do **something**, but he didn't even begin to know how to set about it.

The shaking hand once more took up the pad. Laboriously he wrote again: **SHE DID THIS TO ME.**

Fred knew who he meant. On the other side of the room, talking to Pam, was the woman he had once called Mam, the woman he had grown to hate. Unbelievably, after all these years, Grace Mary was still living with his Dad and still whining and complaining about her lot. He heard her now scrounging from Pam and he saw Pam open her bag and take out five pounds. The grasping fingers closed quickly around the notes.

Fred turned his attention to John Airey. He saw with a jolt that he had again been writing. He read with a sense of shock: **SHE LOST ME £5,000 AT THAT PUB.**

But Grace Mary wasn't looking. She had gone through to the kitchen to make a pot of tea.

Helpless to do anything Fred indicated to Pam that they had better sit down and wait. About to lower himself into a chair he paused, a gasp of surprise escaping him.

Pam looked at him. 'What is it?'

He wasn't sure how much John Airey could hear or understand but he had to share this with his new wife.

'Look!' He whispered. 'Come and look at this.'

Pam stood beside him.

'See that.' Fred pointed to the marks still showing clear and undeniable on the leather covering of the arm of the chair. 'That's were **she** once laid into me with a leather strap.' They gazed down at the square cut caused by the strap his Mam had used on him way back in 1936. Unbelievably it had stayed there for twenty two years - evidence that he had not imagined the cruelty.

'That's what happened when she hit me,' he repeated quietly.

Pam's looked at him in horror. Now the truth became a reality. He had told her only some of the things from his past, but somehow this single piece of evidence said it all. Quietly, she slipped her hand into his.

As soon as they decently could, they left the house. Sickened by what they had witnessed and learned Fred couldn't get away quick enough.

As they walked back to the car he held Pam's arm close to his side, finding comfort in her nearness.

'That's it,' he said. 'I shan't go back again. My Dad's not long for this world and I'm damned if I'm going to take on looking after her.'

'Was it true?' Pam asked. 'What he wrote?'

How was he to know? It could have been the bewildered wanderings of a sick man. The two strokes which Grace had confirmed could have disturbed his mind, affected his memory. But whatever else, it had come across to him clearly, the loathing his Dad now felt for her.

Could love change so much? For once, long ago, John Airey must have felt much as he now did for Pam. Filled with hope and a kind of ecstasy, wanting to spend the rest of their lives together. Ready to take on the whole world.

He stopped and pulled Pam round in front of him. 'I'll always love you,' he said gruffly. 'And if ever I begin to behave casual, or in an uncaring way you just tell me, or box me ears or somethin'.'

She went easily into his arms. She had no doubts at all.

1959

Fred walked across the Tarmac towards doors of the Maternity Home, Haverstock Hill in Hampstead. It was almost seven o'clock in the evening. He would have come sooner if they had allowed it, but the ward sister had been adamant. Visiting was at seven and you didn't argue.

He wasn't sure what he had expected. He had never known anyone closely who had had a baby before. Pam's mother had died with multiple sclerosis when she was nineteen so there had been no older woman to give advice - on the other hand it meant there hadn't been anyone to fill their heads with wicked old wives tales either.

Of course he knew Pam was alright. She was strong as an ox and she had wanted this baby so much. He hadn't been able to put into words what it meant to him. Now at last he was part of a **real** family. **HIS** family. A son to carry his name on down through the centuries.

He was walking through corridors of glass, hearing the sound of his own shoes on the lino. With dozens of tiny babies trying to sleep he suddenly had the feeling he ought to take his shoes off. He grinned to himself, he was getting fanciful again, it was that blessed imagination of his.

Pam had heard him coming, recognising his step. Sitting up in bed, dressed in a new nightie with her dark crisp curly hair outlined against the pillows she looked so lovely she almost took his breath away.

'Hello, love.' His mouth brushed hers, he was scared to kiss her too enthusiastically. He dropped the bunch of flowers he had been carrying onto the bed. 'How are you?'

'I'm fine.' She saw his eyes move away, searching the cot beside the bed.

'Go on, take a look. That's your baby son.'

His son. But his hands were so tiny, he had no eye brows, and his eyes were so tightly shut he couldn't even begin to guess at the colour of them.

'Is he...is he alright?' he asked.

'Perfect. What do you think of him?'

'Oh Pam!' He felt his voice tremble. 'He's smashing. A real little Brayshay.'

'You can pick him up. He won't break.' She made it sound the most natural thing in the world, as if she'd always known exactly how to be a mother.

Oh so carefully he unwrapped the soft blue blankets. His son was dressed in a white nightgown hiding his legs and feet. With infinite care he lifted him into his arms, feeling the reassuring weight, the soft warmness of the tiny body. The baby had a strange unfamiliar smell.

Slowly, as if it had been prearranged, the little eye lids opened and for an instant it seemed to Fred that his son looked at him and knew who he was.

'Hello son,' he said, and with bowed head he touched his lips to the small smooth brow.

It was ridiculous, he felt so proud. The precious hour galloped by. He wished he could pick them both up in his arms and take them home, right there and then.

'I'll be home before you know it,' Pam said, as if reading his thoughts. 'Now next time you come in can you bring......'

She dragged him back to the practicalities of being a new father. The nurse, sympathetic but firm, was insisting now that he really must leave. With the other fathers he made his way back to the entrance.

As he walked to the car he felt as if his heart would burst with happiness. Everything that had ever happened to him, all the hardships, the challenges, the despair, the longing for a real family of his own was as nothing - for now he had everything. His cup truly runneth over.

I am, without a doubt, he thought, quite the happiest man in the world.

Note: Fred was to have two further children after David. Christine in 1961 and Glenn in 1970.

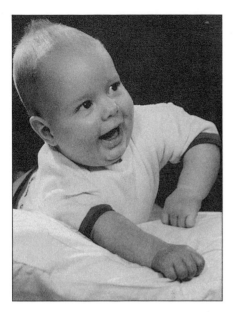

David 1959

Glenn 1970

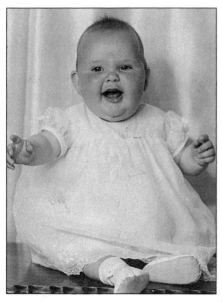

Christine 1961

139

Chapter 10

BLOOD RELATIVES

September 1990

Fred put his foot down. A sense of urgency made him want to push the car to its maximum. As he drove North he recalled with some irony that fiasco with Arthur Banks more than fourteen years ago. Ah, but the difference now was that he had the written evidence, this time he **knew** his destination was Ripon. He knew for sure that his name had been Tew before they turned him into a Brayshay, and he knew his birthplace, stated undeniably on the birth certificate. He fingered it in his pocket, still marvelling that a little piece of paper could make so much difference.

With a sigh he realised that he didn't have to answer to anyone. He would take as long as was necessary to upturn all those stones hiding - well, who knew what? He asked only for the truth. Nothing could hurt him now, not after all these years.

Approaching Langthorpe he slowed down - this was where, he now knew from the birth certificate, his natural mother had lived and worked. The true beginning of his journey back in time started here.

The old village was so little. Rows of houses marched unpretentiously down either side of the lane. At the end of the village there was now a motorway bridge with its ceaseless thundering of vehicles shaking the houses to their foundations. It wouldn't be surprising, Fred thought, if the folk in the cemetery didn't turn in their graves.

THE CEMETERY - of course! Surely it was the best place to start? If there had been Tews who lived and died in Langthorpe, then perhaps some were buried here. It was worth a search.

Was it a stroke of luck that the vicar happened to be there in the porch fiddling with sheaves of papers, looking a bit distracted? Not, Fred admitted to himself, quite the way he expected a vicar to look. Fred cleared his throat. 'Excuse me. I wonder if you can help? I'm trying to trace a family by the name of Tew.' His voice dragged the man's attention away from his fumblings. 'Do you have any people buried here in the church yard by that name?'

Vague blue eyes looked at him, at first not seeming to comprehend. Then, with a visible effort he asked, 'Tew? Tew you say?'

'Yes.' What was wrong with the man?

'Well, I don't think so.' He spoke with a sort of refined north country accent. 'I'm not certain. Though you're very welcome to look.' He turned away.

Fred placed his hand on the shiny black material of his cassock. 'I've come a long way,' he said.

'I'm sorry.' A frown creased the clerical brow. 'But this is my last week here. I'm retiring.'

Retiring? He didn't look old enough. Or was it because he was so vague that he gave this impression? Fancy not knowing who was buried in his own church yard. You'd think if he'd been there for twenty or thirty years he'd have had time to walk around the place a few times and get to know the people who were, in a manner of speaking, his neighbours...even if they were six feet under.

A smile hovered at the corner's of Fred's mouth. Thank God his sense of humour hadn't deserted him.

'All right, vicar,' he said. 'You get on with sorting your things out. I'll take a look around. Oh, and good luck with the retirement.'

As he walked away the smile broke loose, bubbling into laughter. That was probably the wrong thing to say to a vicar, he mused. The clergy didn't believe in luck, did they? Wasn't everything in their eyes supposed to be an act of God, or the devil? Fred wondered which of the two was keeping him company as he bent forward trying to read the worn names on the grave stones once carved with mastery and pride.

Some of them looked quite drunken as they keeled precariously to one side; others, more recently erected, stood straight, appearing strangely out of place amongst the ancient slabs of marble and stone.

Systematically reading the names, he recognised some of the good old fashioned Yorkshire ones. The dates just now were of no interest to him. He could investigate the history of Langthorpe some other time. All he wanted was to find that one name - TEW.

But there were none, though he searched diligently. Feeling a bit deflated Fred returned to the church. The vicar had disappeared.

In the village he began knocking on doors, asking over and over again if someone, anyone, could help him.

It wasn't until he stopped to get a drink and eat a sandwich that he had the opportunity to search the local telephone directory.

Suddenly it all seemed too easy. There was a Tew listed and the address, 8 Hill View. Fred glanced at his watch. It was 6 p.m.. Surely not too late to pay a visit, and if M.Tew went to work, well, he or she should be home by now.

It was the strangest feeling, curiosity tinged with a kind of apprehension, wanting so much for this to be the right place, the right people, wondering how they'd receive him, even if they would believe him. If his mother had had him illegitimately, and it sounded very much as if she may have - for, in Fred's mind, there was no other reason he could think of why he had been born in a work house and adopted - then the chances were that no one in the family had ever heard of him, or if they had, they might not be prepared to admit it.

I wonder if the old lady is alive? I wonder if I do have a mother? Will she acknowledge me or deny me? What havoc is my visit likely to create?

Had he the right to thrust this situation on someone after sixty two years? And had she wondered, ever wondered what had happened to him. It was just remotely possible that she had in some way kept in touch and he had known nothing about it.

He looked at number 8 Hill View. It could have been a modern bungalow anywhere in the country. Realising he had been standing staring down at it from the road for some time, and not knowing who was watching from behind net curtains, he squared his shoulders, stepped up to the door and ran the bell.

The door opened and Fred found himself confronted by a man who looked anything but pleased to see him. Even before he spoke Fred was aware of the likeness; but for the fact that this man was slightly balding, and somewhat shorter, their features, complexions, eyes, all added to his conviction that this time he had hit the jackpot.

Fred cleared his throat. His voice was husky at the best of times, it wasn't helped now by the conflicting emotions poised ready to explode inside his head. 'Mr Tew?' he asked.

'Yes?' As he looked at Fred he began to move his jaws, behaving for all the world as if he'd been disturbed in the middle of a meal.

Fred asked, 'I wonder if you could spare me a few minutes?'

'I'm having my dinner.' He chewed more deliberately, defying Fred to contradict or dare to disturb a man occupied in the business of eating.

'I'm sorry. I'll call back later.' Fred turned as if to go.

'Wait a minute. What is it you're trying to sell?' His suspicion of window glazing men and the like heightened the man's defensive posture.

'I'm not selling anything,' Fred assured him. 'But don't let me disturb you, I can come back later.'

'No, wait. What's this all about?'

Fred's fingers closed around the birth certificate in the bottom of his pocket. 'My name's Fred Brayshay,' he said. 'I have reason to believe we may be related.'

'Related?' Doubt flickered in the man's eyes. 'Where do you come from?'

'I've driven up from Somerset. Taunton to be exact.'

The door opened wider. 'You'd better come in,' he said.

Fred was lead into a clean cheerful room and asked to take a seat. Sitting on the edge of a chair, hands resting on his knees, the man looked with open curiosity into Fred's face.

'See a likeness do you?' Fred passed him the birth certificate. 'I'm Elsie Tew's son.'

'Good Lord above! Elsie! Though she's not called Tew anymore.' Slowly he scrutinising the typed details.

Fred watched and waited. Would they throw him out? Would they curse the day they let him over the doorstep - or would they understand?

After what seemed a long time he looked up from the birth certificate and his eyes met Fred's. 'My name's Mervyn,' he said slowly. 'My father was Elsie's brother.'

'Did you know that she'd had a son? That I was adopted?' He pulled out the adoption papers. 'It's all down here in black and white.'

A comfortable looking lady with a Hertfordshire accent came into the room. 'My wife, Barbara,' Mervyn said simply.

They shook hands and Fred saw the question held there in her eyes. 'I'm your husband's cousin,' he explained. 'I've only just found this out for myself. It's all a bit of a shock.'

'No one ever knew.' Mervyn stared at him, disbelief still written on his face. 'In all these years no one has ever spoken of a son. Certainly not Elsie. This is quite incredible. But why have you decided to come back now? What did you expect to find?'

Fred sat back, looking from Mervyn to his wife, trying to assess their response. He wondered what on earth they must be thinking.

'I suppose,' he said, 'deep down inside all of us is the desire to know our roots. What sort of family we come from. I guess I needed to know why I was given away. Why I was born in a work house.'

They made tea, chatting more freely now.

Fred attempted to impart his feelings. 'My wife died last year. After she'd gone I had this compelling desire to find my family. It was there in my head all the time. It wouldn't go away. I've been drifting a bit. After thirty odd years of marriage...well, it's not easy to adjust. Somehow I felt I had to go back and complete some unfinished business.' He sat back. 'That's why I'm here.'

'How...how did you find us?' Barbara came into the conversation. 'I mean...well, your name's Brayshay you say.'

'The law changed some years ago. You can get the information now that used once to be kept secret. I always had this thought I'd something to do with Richmond in North Yorks and that my mother's name was Mary Tew. I found out I was wrong. I could remember quite clearly the years I'd spent with my adoptive parents in Cliviger, but before that...well...I just didn't know. Since I found out it was Ripon and not Richmond I've been putting two and two together and hoping I didn't come up with five.'

Mervyn said, 'The next logical step is to get mother up here. I'll go and fetch her, she's not on the phone. She'll be able to tell you far more than we can.'

Fred asked, 'Do you know...is it possible my mother's still alive?'

'She was. The last we heard she was living in Salisbury,' Mervyn told him. 'But Mother will be able to tell you more.' And then, with a cheerful smile, he left the house and went to fetch the old lady.

Barbara looked shyly at Fred. 'He looks like you,' she said. 'I can't deny the family likeness. I think he's pleased you've come.'

'You don't think it's an intrusion?'

'You had to know. I'd have wanted to.' She smiled, her eyes kind, reassuring.

Mervyn returned with the look of a conjuror who has surprised the audience. 'Here she is,' he said. 'She couldn't believe it when I told her.'

She sailed into the room, which was an achievement in itself, for she was portly and getting on in years. Fred calculated that she must have been have been between seventy and seventy five. A wonderful positive cheerful lady. She made you feel better just to look at her.

'This is my mother, Glady's,' Mervyn said.

'So you say you're Elsie's lad.' She looked at Fred, her eyes bright and openly curious. 'What a turn up for the books this is!'

'I know very little,' he told her. 'I'm hoping some of you can help fill in the gaps.'

'You know you have a half-sister?'

Fred's heart seemed to miss a beat. This was something he hadn't even considered. 'Alive?' he asked.

She nodded. 'As far as I know.'

This was a real piece of news - so unexpected. 'How old would she be?'

No! It wasn't possible! This bright happy lady was sitting here telling him that he had a sister five years his senior. It couldn't be! If he accepted that, then it followed that his mother had kept her and given him away.

The pain, he realised, must have shown in his face. He turned his eyes away. Picking up his third cup of tea he diverted his attention, waiting for calm to return.

But Mervyn had noticed. 'Didn't she live with the grandmother?' he asked his mother gently, as the family history played hide-and-seek with his memory. 'I don't think Elsie actually **kept** her, did she?'

Nodding to herself, pleased that she was able to tell them, Gladys said, 'Yes, that's right. It was the grannie as kept her. Elsie went into service or somethin'. No...wait, I remember, she went to work for a doctor.'

'And then?' Fred leaned forward. He didn't want to rush her. He had to get the story right. There was always the danger that under pressure people began to invent, to elaborate in a desire to please or hold the attention of the listener.

The old lady paused, searching her memory, plucking one out of the vast wealth of experiences, examining it a for a moment and then discarding it. Finally she said, 'It's a funny thing, but the way I remember it, she left that job and then seemed to disappear for some time. No one knew what had happened to her, or else they weren't saying. I wonder.....'

Fred said nothing. But the thoughts crystallized in his mind; was it possible the doctor she'd worked for had been his father? It wasn't unheard of for the man of the house to get the maid in the family way and put her somewhere with enough money to see her through that 'difficult' period.

But his father hadn't even done that. Pregnant and disgraced, she must have found her way to the workhouse.

Of course he was only speculating, he supposed he liked the idea of being a doctor's son, even if he had abandoned him.

A young girl slipped unobtrusively into the room; sitting down on the settee she stared at him with an inquisitive expression. She'd been listening quietly, and obviously wondering about this strange turn of events. Now she said, 'I couldn't help hearing. And I think you do rather look like Dad.'

'This is Beverly, one of our daughters.' Mervyn introduced this bright eyed, friendly girl. 'We've got Louise as well, but she's married now so we don't see so much of her.'

There was that instant recognition that sometimes happens between two people as Fred and Beverly looked at each other. We already understand, the look seemed to say, there'll never be a problem between us. We're two of a kind. He wondered if she was consciously aware of it.

145

'Your eyes are just like Dad's,' she said and smiled at him.

'And he's got the Tew neck. Thick neck. Built like a bull,' Mervyn said and they all laughed.

Gladys was fishing in a volumous bag. 'I've brought some photos. Let's have a look. See if the likeness is there in any of the rest of the family. It'll give you a better idea what they look like anyway. It must be a queer feelin', findin' you have relatives after all this time.'

It was indeed the strangest feeling, sitting there looking at the faces of those strangers who were supposed to be his mother and sister.

This photograph, taken in the 70s, was given to Fred by Gladys. It shows from left to right, his real mother, his half-sister Ethel and Gladys.

He explained about his own three children, hoping Mervyn and his family would understand how much it had meant to him, never having had a real family before. Dave the eldest was now 32 he told them, and Christine was 28. 'Oh, yes, and I'm a grandad.' He sounded proud and knew it. 'Little Jamie Lee. She's three and the joy of my life.'

He looked at their faces. Rather shyly he added, 'I'd like you to meet them all one day.'

'You're lucky,' said Barbara, with an expression that said she was looking forward to having grandchildren of her own.

'And then there's young Glenn,' Fred continued, 'He's twenty. He still lives with me but half the time we drive each other round the bend. It's difficult to stretch across all those years and appreciate each other's life style and point of view.'

'But you love them,' Barbara said with understanding.

'They're my world.' Fred breathed deeply. 'But that's wrong. They have to get on with their own lives and me with mine. Finding out all this is going to help, I'm sure.'

Simultaneously they became conscious of the time. They had talked for hours and hours and drunk gallons of tea.

'What do you want to do?' Mervyn asked. 'I expect you'd like to look around a bit before you leave.'

Beverly bounced up. 'I'll go and phone. See if I can book you in somewhere for a night or two.'

Fred looked at her gratefully. She didn't want him to go yet. None of them did. It was a really nice feeling. 'If it's not too much bother,' he said.

Gladys was trying to fill in the details of his half-sister. 'She married somebody called Lou. An' I do recall she still used to see her mother before we lost touch. Oddly enough she seemed to dote on her mother.'

Her smiley face clouded over. 'I don't know where they are now, not Elsie or your sister Ethel. They were in Salisbury last time I heard.'

'Well, I've certainly got plenty to be going on with.' He stood up. 'I appreciate your time, and for making me so welcome. I hope you don't think it was too much of an imposition.''

'Nonsense,' Mervyn told him. 'We've enjoyed it. Can't really take it in yet though.'

He stepped outside. 'I'll drive down in front of you and show you the way. This hotel's a fair distance and you won't want to get lost.'

'See you tomorrow,' Mervyn called as they parted. 'I'm off sick from work at present so I'll be around. Call any time.'

Fred stood in the strange bedroom. It was a really nice place. Thirty quid a night, and that covered a good breakfast. Well, that wouldn't break the bank. Maybe he would stay a couple of nights. He'd wait and see how things went.

He lay quietly between the clean white sheets, there were still a hundred questions he wanted to ask, places he must visit, people he'd like to try and trace. He didn't expect to sleep at all.....

When he awoke at seven o'clock he realised with a jolt that he had slept deeply and undisturbed. He couldn't remember when he'd last had such a good night.

It was odd, he'd always said he would never leave Somerset, that it was home to him now. But since he'd arrived in Langthorpe he'd been experiencing such a comfortable feeling - well, it made him wonder, perhaps after all there was something indefinable, instinctive almost, in this feeling about where you belonged.

Autumn, still warm, greeted him with a rush of air as he left the hotel. But it wasn't any more than the constant flow of heavy traffic whisking the leaves up into the air.

Parking his car in Ripon he made his way to the old workhouse. It had to be his first stop. This is where it all started...his beginnings...once a bulge beneath the skirts of a girl called Elsie. With nowhere to go, frightened, desperate, ashamed, she must have found her way to this building.

There must have been a time when she lay on a bed writhing and panting whilst he struggled to be free of her, out into his world. And what a world it had proved to be!

He sat on a garden wall contemplating the building. It was a monstrosity, Fred thought; an enormous dismal grey stone place covered in grime. God it must have been hell to be shut up in there with no hope - no hope at all.

A man, pottering in the garden on the other side of the wall where he sat pondering, looked curiously in his direction.

Fred nodded. 'Mornin'. Nice to see a bit of grass.' He indicated the lawn. 'Been here long?'

'A tidy time. I live in one of them flats.' He pointed to the blank faces of the block of buildings behind him.

'Do you know anything about that place?' Fred asked, nodding in the direction of the Old Workhouse.

'Aye. It's the probation offices and social security building or something like that.' He straightened up and began to roll a cigarette. 'You a stranger round here?'

'Kind of. Though actually I was born there.'

'In the probation offices?' He stared at Fred, amazed.

'It wasn't offices then. In fact it was a workhouse. Did you now it then?'

'No. Never heard anybody say it was either. Must have been before my time.'

Fred found himself grinning. 'Well, maybe before you came to this place.'

He could find out nothing more though he chatted to the man for some time. Standing, he stretched his legs and arms. 'I think I'll walk over there and take a look for myself.'

'Well, good luck to you. I hope you find what you're lookin' for.'

Fred ventured into the quadrangle of the grim building. Slowly, curiously, he walked in through the doorway.

Pausing there he looked around, seeing the office marked 'Enquiries'. Ah well, that was as good as place as any other to start.

The ladies in the office were charming and appeared to be genuinely interested in what he told them. He had a very positive feeling that they wanted to help. They answered his questions without making him feel in any way awkward.

One left her position and joined him. 'I'll show you around,' she said. 'I expect you'd like to see the cells. They're still here on the ground floor.'

She preceded him through the building explaining things to him in just the way she might have done had she been escorting him around some baronial home; her words were interspersed with the opening and closing of doors.

At one door she stopped, looked at Fred and said, 'Here we are. This is where the babies were born.'

Fred stared into the room. A shiver racked his body; after sixty two years he had come full circle. In this room, or one just like it, he had struggled into the world. The woman was right, they were nothing more than cells, but he could smell the dank misery all around him as if it had been indelibly imprinted upon the walls.

Now he wanted only to get out into the open air. Hastily he thanked the woman; disciplining himself not to break into a run he walked beside her back into the main lobby.

'Thank you,' he said again. 'You've been most helpful.'

Outside he breathed deeply. He looked about him, holding on to the signs of modern living all around him, grasping at the framework, reassuring himself of his existence.

Calm settled gently back into his heart. Finally he made a decision. He would go to the library next and see if they had any information there.

For hours he searched, once more thumbing through records and documents, but there was no mention of the time the workhouse ceased to function or when its use had been changed to one more acceptable to the people of post war Britain. Perhaps

Ripon had been ashamed of it, or perhaps, to the town, it was simply of no importance.

'Only a silly old codger like me would want to know,' he said aloud.

Several hours into the day the thought kept coming back to him - what a dump, it really is an awful place. There's nothing nice to say about it at all; the streets are overflowing with stinking traffic - he watched it for a moment hurling itself along in an endless whirl of frenetic activity - the buildings are grey with nothing to commend them, there's not a tree in sight and yet, I feel so...oh, I don't know. I'll go back to Mervyn's and invite them to have dinner with me tonight at the hotel.

The welcome he received made him feel really good. It was as if already he was part of their family. What lovely people.

Beverley was going through a minor crisis. She was off on holiday at the weekend to Yugoslavia. 'I've never been abroad before,' she told him. 'Suppose I don't like the idea of flying?'

'You'll love it,' Fred assured her. 'There's nothing to it.'

'Just keep a close watch on your handbag,' her mother said.

Mervyn added, 'And watch your luggage. Don't let it out of your sight.'

Beverly was switching from one foot to the other, her fingers hovering at her lips as if she sought reassurance from the contact. 'But they take your luggage off you. You can't very well put it on your lap in the plane.'

Barbara shook her head. 'You've nothing to worry about. Only watch the men. Them foreigners think they can get away with anything. Just keep saying no.'

Fred wanted laugh. It seemed so funny to him, the natural way they spoke in front of him.

'It'll be alright, Beverly,' he said quietly.

'You're sure?'

'I'm sure.'

It was with enormous pleasure he discovered that Mervyn was an amateur artist. It seemed to link them together - almost as if he felt the gift ran in the family - endorsing the feeling of belonging.

'Let's have a look then, Mervyn. I'd love to see some of your work, really I would.'

Barbara laughed. 'You'll wish you hadn't said that. He's got hundreds of them.'

When Fred saw them he realised she hadn't been joking. The bedroom walls were lined with paintings, they were stacked in heaps wherever there was space.

Fred looked at them. His eyebrows rose with surprise. This was not the work of an amateur. Mervyn was truly talented - and the detail he had put into them.... He felt as if he could almost reach over and dip his fingers into the water of the river in that painting with the cathedral.

'But Mervyn! They're good!' Fred exclaimed. 'Very good. Why on earth don't you sell them?'

'I never thought..well...that anyone would want to buy them.'

'Well I would for a start.' Fred had already fallen for the one with the foaming river. 'How much do you want for that? How long did it take you to do?'

They agreed a price, both men grinning at each other. It may have been the start of a new career for Mervyn; from his expression he was suddenly seeing the possibility of making money out of doing something that he truly loved.

Fred carried the painting out to the car. It was time for him to be heading back. 'Come again,' they said. 'Any time. Now don't you forget.'

As if he ever could. You don't find a family after sixty two years and then forget about it. Oh, he would be back. He wanted to see them all again - often.

He had yet to experience the extraordinary phone call which was to come from Mervyn.

Fred with his cousin Mervyn and wife Barbara - the first blood relative he finds

Chapter 11

REJECTION

'It's your birthday, Dad. What do you want to do about it?' Fred listened to Christine's voice on the phone.

Was it really only four days since he had been in Harrogate and that nice woman had handed him his birth certificate? Could he really have experienced so much in so short a time?

'I've a lot to tell you, Chrissie,' he said. 'What about the two of us going out to dinner? We can celebrate and I'll tell you all about what's been happening to me up in Yorkshire.'

'I'll have to bring Jamie Lee with me.'

Jamie Lee, his granddaughter. He seemed to melt at the thought of her - in an instant he held in front of him a mental picture of her round face, her intelligent searching eyes, always wanting to know everything.

'Yes, bring Jamie Lee,' he heard himself say.

The meal was finished. Fred felt as if he had been talking for a long time. 'So that's about it.' He leaned back and looked at his daughter across the table. 'What do you think?'

'It's hard to believe.' Her dark eyes sparkled as she looked into his face. 'You're really pleased, aren't you?'

'Yes. I've found a real live blood relation. Mervyn's my cousin, and that makes all his family our family. I want you to meet them, Chrissie. They are lovely people.'

'Perhaps I will, one day.' For a moment she hesitated and then said gently, 'But it doesn't really mean much to me, Dad. I've got you and Dave and Glenn, and my Jamie Lee. I don't feel I need any more people in my life.'

'Oh!' He tried to hide his disappointment. 'Well, I guess I understand.' But he didn't. He couldn't see how she wasn't as excited as he felt to know she had a family with cousins and an aunt and maybe even a grandmother.

'I've got to get back now, Dad. It's time Jamie Lee was in bed.'

Fred called for the bill. She had tried to show interest, he'd grant her that. But he could see it meant little to her; as far as she was concerned they were just some folk he'd discovered who lived in the north.

Glenn's interest was virtually non-existent, even less enthusiastic. He seemed more interested in his car.

I'll go and see Dave, Fred decided, refusing to allow his feelings to be dampened. Dave's older and more mature, he'll understand. I'm sure he'll want to meet them.

Was it an unconscious thing, this decision? Slowly it filtered through to the conscious part of his brain: when he visited Dave in Portsmouth it wouldn't be too out of the way to call in at Salisbury - maybe his real mother **was** still alive - at least someone may remember her.

Mervyn's mother had given him the last known address, he folded the paper into his diary. Yes, he mused, he might just go and at least have a look at the place.

Salisbury is a beautiful city with graceful spires of the cathedral reaching up into the sky and soft green lawns and trees setting it apart from the rest of the bustle of life.

He found the building - it was an unimpressive block of flats. Gladys had told him that after his mother married her name had become Truswell, with this knowledge he began knocking on doors. His lips formed themselves into a wry smile, this door knocking was almost getting to be a habit.

But the responses were once more negative: 'No, sorry. I only moved here a few months ago.'

'I'm not buying anything.' A door slammed in his face.

'No. Never heard of her. You could try Alice Cooper, she's been here the longest.'

Another door. Another bell. Another moment of holding his breath hoping and yet in a way not hoping, for he had come away from Gladys with a strange disquieting feeling about Elsie, his half-sister, and someone called Lou. Funny, because if anyone had asked him, he couldn't have explained what it was.

Alice Cooper was in. Nodding and smiling she said. 'Oh, yes, I remember them. I lived right next door. Last thing I heard the old lady was in a nursing home. There was a daughter called Ethel and her husband, Lou.'

'Do you know where they are now?' Fred asked.

'I believe I can give you a telephone number. Just wait a minute.'

Fred walked away, holding yet another piece of paper in his hands. Maybe he'd ring, he would have a think about it. He recognised that he wasn't yet ready to commit himself - not all the way. Supposing it proved disastrous? Suppose there was open hostility and resentment? Suppose his mother didn't want to know him?

Driving away from Salisbury, aware suddenly of gnawing hunger pains, Fred pulled into a Motorchef and stopped the engine.

From where he sat in the café eating he could see the phone box outside. It seemed to be yelling at him:

What are you waiting for? You haven't come this far for nothing, have you?

I'm on my way to see Dave in Portsmouth.

But you want to know.

I'm not sure.

Then phone and find out.

I suppose a phone call wouldn't hurt.

Go ON then.

I don't have much change.

You've enough.

She could be dead. They might resent my intrusion. They don't even know that I exist.

You'll spend the rest of your life regretting it if you don't make this phone call.

He lifted the receiver and dialled.

Fred cleared his throat. 'Who's speaking?'

'Lou here. Who's that?'

'You won't know me. I wonder...' How the hell did he broach the subject? 'Is it possible...did you ever hear that your wife had a brother?'

'WHAT?'

'My name's Frederick Brayshay. Actually...well, I believe I may be your wife's half-brother. I got your number from Alice Cooper in Salisbury this morning.'

'So what do you want?' The voice, crisp and authoritative sounded abrupt, almost dismissive.

'Is...is the old lady still alive?'

'Yes, she is.' There was a pause and then he continued, 'But she doesn't know anyone half the time.'

'I...I would...that is...I've never seen her. I suppose she never spoke about me?'

'Never. But as I say, she's very ill. She's got altzimer's disease. Her mind is all

154

mixed up. It wouldn't be right for you to see her - not now - not with her like this.'

Fred's eye was on the telephone, he had no more change and he was about to run out. 'Can I give you my telephone number. I'm from Taunton. If you wouldn't mind ...just in case something happens and you want to contact me.'

'Alright then.'

Fred rattled it off, hearing the click and burr as they were disconnected. A terrible feeling of impotence overwhelmed him. After all he had been through - to get this far and to be told it wouldn't be right for him to see the old lady.

What about **his** rights? Didn't he have any? Hadn't he ever had any?

Bitterness engulfed him. Had all the struggling been for nothing?

He sat for a long time staring blindly into space, trying to make sense of it all. But there was neither rhyme nor reason to life, no bloody purpose at all. You just lived and died and that was all there was to it. For the hundredth time since Pam died he felt himself wanting to quit everything...then...he remembered Dave.

He was supposed to be on his way to see his son. HIS son. Of course there was purpose and meaning! What was he thinking about? Didn't he have three wonderful kids and a gorgeous granddaughter?

He switched on the ignition, hearing at the same moment one of his favourite tunes on the car radio. It was one he and Pam had always loved. Humming quietly to himself he slipped the car into gear.

'But, Dad! I don't want to be anyone else. I'm Dave Brayshay, that's who I am. I can't suddenly start thinking of myself as a Tew. I don't want to know about a family we've had nothing to do with in the whole of our lives.'

His good humoured face was flushed as he stared back at his father. 'Don't you see? That's all in the past. It may be part of your history but it's not ours.'

Fred swirled the beer round in his glass struggling to come to terms with this latest revelation: Christine hadn't been too interested though she'd tried, but Dave was actively hostile towards the whole idea.

'Alright, Dave, let's drop it for now. But perhaps one day you wouldn't mind meeting Mervyn and his family, to please me, son.'

'One day perhaps,' Dave looked at his father and the warmth in his smile drew Fred close. No matter how he felt, he was his boy - he always would be.

'Fancy a game of darts?' Dave asked.

The next day, after Dave had left his flat for work, Fred decided to start for home. His talk with Dave, plus Lou's reaction when he'd phoned, had really clinched things. He wasn't going to attempt to see Elsie Tew - he pictured her now only as some confused old woman in a nursing home and realised he had no place in her life. Well, that was nothing new, he never had.

Back in Taunton with its familiar streets, its back drop of soft green hills and woods, he began to pick up again the routine of his everyday life: it seemed like he had reached the end of the trail.

Chapter 12

THE FUNERAL

Fred leaned back in his arm chair, the screen before him held his full attention as he watched Ian Woosnam tee up on the final hole. There was only one thought in his head, he wished he could play golf just half an well as the man on television.

The phone rang. Muttering under his breath Fred reached out and lifted the receiver.

'Fred? Hello! Mervyn here.'

'Hello, Mervyn. How's everyone?'

'We're alright thanks. But I thought you'd want to know...we've just heard...the old lady's passed away. Lou's going to ring you.'

For a moment Fred was speechless. What did he feel? What was he supposed to say? After his conversation with Lou more than six months ago it seemed incredible that his half-sister's husband should now be telephoning him.

'I had the feeling he didn't want anything to do with me,' he replied cautiously.

Mervyn's voice, calm, sensible, blessedly reassuring came back to him. 'I'm sure they were just trying to protect the old lady, Fred. You must admit, it was a delicate situation.'

'Oh! I see! Well, I can understand that. I'll just wait till he rings then.'

'I'll speak to you again soon,' Mervyn said and the line went dead.

In silence, he sat waiting. Of course the man might change his mind - it could be hours before he got in touch. Why did Lou want to speak to him anyway? What was there to say? It was all over. His mother was dead.

Five minutes later he lifted the receiver to hear Ethel's voice addressing him. This was his half-sister - a woman he'd never met and until recently never even knew that she existed. What a weird feeling. In sixty odd years he had had a sister and this was the first time he had heard her voice. It was peculiar, for in a strange way it sounded familiar. There was no logical reason why it should be so or even ought to be, but the fact was, he felt he recognised it.

'Fred? Fred Brayshay? This is Ethel, your sister.'

'Yes?' He hesitated, aware that the next move had to come from her.

'I'm sorry to have to tell you that mother's died.'

He could hardly believe his ears. She was referring to her as if they were jointly involved, including him as if he had always been part of their family.

'Oh, I'm sorry to hear it.' He tried to make his voice sound sympathetic. 'How are you keeping?'

He heard the break in her voice as she replied, 'I've not been at all well...the doctor's put me on tablets. I've been very depressed.'

What did he want to hear? That his mother had asked for him. Could her wandering mind have gone back to that workhouse where he was born? Did she make her peace with her God before her spirit left this earth? Had she still, after all these years, been sorry that she had given away her baby son?

Then to Fred's astonishment Ethel said: 'The funeral's on Tuesday at Salisbury crematorium at eleven o'clock. I would like you to be there.'

Fred felt his stomach begin to churn. There didn't seem any point. He had never seen her - he'd never known her - to him Elsie Tew was as a stranger.

'I'd like you to be there.' Ethel's voice sounded strained, as if she was finding this conversation difficult.

'I see,' he replied, though in truth he didn't see at all. He couldn't even begin to imagine why now, when it was all over, they should want to meet him.

And then she said the most extraordinary thing. 'I really feel you ought to come.'

'You do?'

'Yes, I do. Please Fred. I need your support. It...it's your duty to come.'

'Well...in that case...' His mind was reeling. His duty? How could it be his duty? Elsie Tew had never been anything to him. What a strange thing to say!

'So you'll come?' She persisted. In some curious way it was now obvious to him that it was Ethel who needed him to be there. He didn't understand it, he couldn't even begin to speculate as to where all this was leading.

Would he go? Did he want to? Or was it better to leave things as they were?

Fred heard the break in her voice and himself saying, 'Yes, alright. I'll come. I'll see if my daughter Chrissie can get the time off to come with me.'

He said his farewell and rang off. He needed time to think. Time for all this to sink in. The incredible fact was that he had just agreed to go to the funeral of a mother he'd never seen, never heard, never knew.

And then the anger came; it spilled over, years and years of longing to be part of a family, wanting to be recognised - and all the while with the growing knowledge that no one wanted him, that no one cared.

Painfully he recalled the time they had told him it wouldn't be right for him to see her, and now here they were telling him it was his duty to attend her funeral. He wanted to hit out, to hurt those who had hurt him, to punish those who had put him in an orphanage and the adoptive mother who had driven him into a home; he thought of the heartless discipline by Nicholson in St George's Home for Waifs and Strays, and he thought of the shame and guilt he had experienced when he had been sent to Buckley Hall - a place where misfits went, boys who were unmanageable, boys who were bad, and he had been made to feel he was one of them, that in some bewildering way he had done something terribly wrong.

For hours he sat there feeling the anger ebb and flow, allowing for the first time his true emotions to have their way.

Slowly, like a cleansing, his mind began to move towards all the positive events in his life; the gift he had been given to draw and paint, the skills he had developed in carpentry and building, the wonderful care he'd received at the hands of Dawson. And now, didn't he have his own family, his own business, friends to be proud of? Perhaps, if life had been too easy he wouldn't have achieved all he had.

How grateful he was when Chrissie said, 'I'll come, Dad. It'll be interesting to meet them.'

It was going to be a whole heap easier going to that funeral if he had one of his own family with him. He wondered what his sister Ethel was actually like. Did she resemble him? Would she talk to him? And could she answer the rest of the questions that remained still unanswered in his brain?

They arrived early at the crematorium. The chapel was eerily deserted. Taking his little granddaughter by the hand Fred quietly lead the way into the building. Outside, with the typical contrariness of English weather, when it ought to have been raining, when it would have felt appropriate for it to be pouring down, it was a beautiful English morning.

Chrissie was looking around curiously. He wondered what she was thinking, if this meant anything to her at all. He acknowledged the courage in her to come, to face these strangers. He felt a surge of warmth and gratitude for her support.

For one moment he found himself wondering if Pam had been still been alive would she have come?

A few people began to filter in, they seated themselves on the other side of the aisle. Later he was to learn they were members of staff from the nursing home where the old lady had been cared for.

Music began to play softly in the background and he stood up abruptly as he saw the coffin being carried in.

159

Fred's eyes searched the faces of those who followed, looking for subtle likenesses that would identify family connections. Yes, that woman must be Ethel, she looked so poorly, and beside her walked a short stocky fellow who was undoubtedly her husband, Lou. Without glancing in their direction the tiny group of mourners walked past, heads bowed.

He stared at the coffin. That's my mother in there, what a curious feeling to be here at the funeral of the woman who brought me into the world - a woman I've never seen or spoken to. He was surprised at his own compassion. Elsie was dead. It was all over. How could anyone ever have guessed, all that long time ago, that the son she had been forced to give away would one day attend her funeral.

But, he silently acknowledged, he was now more interested in his living relatives. He waited patiently for the simple service to come to an end. Every so often Chrissie would catch his eye and smile. Jamie Lee climbed up on his lap perplexed by her strange surroundings. 'Grandad?' she said.

He stroked her head. 'All right darling. Be quiet for just a bit longer and then Grandad will play with you.'

Outside Ethel stood waiting to speak to those who had attended. She shook his hand, uttered a few words and turned away.

With Chrissie and little Jamie Lee he moved towards the car park. It occurred to him that he didn't know where to go. He supposed he was expected to go back to the house, after all Ethel had told him he ought to attend the funeral.

He had followed the others when they drove back to the house, now he parked his car in the street behind the line of cars and climbed out. Gently he pushed his daughter ahead of him up to the plain front door.

Indoors they sat awkwardly in a row, drinking cups of tea and eating sandwiches. Ethel began to talk about the past, actively including him in her conversation.

One of her daughters-in-law leaned forward and gripped Ethel's hands, drawing her attention. 'Mum,' she said. 'That's Fred, your brother you are talking to - don't you remember, he wasn't there. He doesn't know what you are talking about.'

She stared at Fred obviously confused. Everything had been too much for her. At close quarters he could see that she looked very much like Christine - or was he imagining it?

He knew now from listening to the rest of the family that even though Ethel's grandmother had actually been given the responsibility of bringing her up, in latter years the mother and daughter had become totally devoted to one other. Where she had gone, Ethel had followed.

Fred turned to her two sons. Here he felt on more familiar ground; they were better able to communicate. Their wives, Fred noted, were chattering comfortably to

Chrissie and before long he realised they had a genuine interest in him and why he was there.

After a while his eyes began to register his surroundings. The furniture crowded into the room gave it a homely atmosphere. On top of a sideboard and spread out amongst the cards of sympathy on the mantle piece were numerous photographs.

Tony, one of the sons, spoke. 'Do you want to know who they are, Fred?' he asked.

Fred and Chrissie both nodded. They looked with interest at the pictures handed to them. And then Fred was holding a photograph of his mother. He gazed for long minutes at the face, wondering. She looked so frail. A stranger to him and yet.....

A glass of wine was pressed quietly into his hand, distracted he returned the picture.

Fred with his half-sister Ethel and her son Tony. Taken after the funeral.
Spring 1991

Several glasses on everyone became more relaxed, the conversation turned to other things and the initial tension disappeared.

Finally Fred caught Christine's eye. Getting the signal she rose. 'We'd better be going,' she said. 'I have to get back before Jamie Lee's bedtime.'

They promised to keep in touch. He shook hands with Ethel and Lou. He wasn't sure how he felt, and that was the strangest feeling of all.

Chrissie, her dark hair gleaming, walked ahead of him out to the car. Her duty accomplished she had only one thought, to return to Taunton and get on with her life.

As he followed, an enormous overwhelming thought possessed his mind - like a sudden rush of adrenalin in response to a life-threatening situation - it reached out to the very roots of his hair, to the tips of his fingers and the ends of his toes; he stopped dead, examining this intrusion, and then, finally he knew - he knew what it was: despite all the documentary evidence he could never be a hundred percent certain - for there was now no one who could tell him - that Elsie Tew was his real mother.

He had been so close to seeing her, so close to asking - but he wouldn't have needed to ask, they would have looked at each other and he would have known - oh, yes, then he would have known that it had been she who had given birth to him all those years ago in the workhouse.

Chapter 13

GOING BACK AGAIN

June 1991

At this time Fred's story was nearing completion. I asked him to go back once more to take photographs in order that we might include them in this book, and to bring any other relevant papers or documents he could find. I also felt the story was incomplete without those first missing eighteen months between leaving the workhouse and being adopted - but then this is a true story and life doesn't have the tidy habit of the fiction story in bringing everything to a satisfactory conclusion; it was inevitable that we would have to leave some queries unanswered. I didn't know what he would discover, but at least, I thought, we should have the photographs.

It was a Friday afternoon when Fred climbed into his car and headed for the motorway. Once in gear the automatic gearbox looked after itself. He enjoyed the countryside; the soft gentleness of a summer that had seen more cloud than sunshine found him singing quietly to himself. I haven't felt so relaxed in years, he mused. I wonder what I'll find this time.

In truth he had no intention of looking for anything more. He planned only to take some photographs, visit Mervyn and his family and spend a few days holiday with his eldest son. He sighed happily, Dave had been a great comfort to him since Pam died.

So what was that niggly thought that flitted illusively through the shadows of his mind? He recognised that there was still a gap - the gnawing mysterious eighteen months between being born in the workhouse and his adoption by John and Grace Brayshay. He must have gone **somewhere** during that time before they took him home to Cliviger. He still seemed to think he had been placed in an orphanage in Leeds, but there was no such place and no records he had been able to unearth proved its earlier existence.

The sight of the main street of Cliviger created in him a warm familiar feeling. He parked his car, knowing this time exactly what he intended to do. Taking out his camera he positioned himself at the end of the road and peered at the tiny picture in the view finder showing the row of houses that made up the Co-operative Buildings. He pressed his finger on the button - an instant and he had recorded a moment frozen in time. Just for old times sake, he told himself, and to please Wendy. The book had been like a therapy in itself, he had never imagined that the research and discoveries would prove so fascinating.

Number three, he noticed, where he had lived with John and Grace Brayshay was for sale. At another house he met a nice woman who was actually taking care of the children for the day who came from Number Three. And then, on the opposite side of the yard (where he had once played on his tricycle and where Mona Pickles had first informed him that he was adopted) he discovered a lady who knew some of the people who had once been neighbours there.

The back yard of the Co-op buildings Cliviger as it is today where Fred played on his tricycle in the 1930s

'I know where Billy Clough lives,' the woman volunteered. 'I could take you down there if you like.'

Billy Clough! Oh yes! Fred remembered Billy. He had been a few years older than the rest of them. So he was still alive, living not much more than a stone's throw away.

On the doorstep they stood staring at each other, recognising beneath the lines of age and greying hair the lads they had once been.

'Come along in,' Billy said, as if it was the most natural thing in the world for him to be standing there. 'Let's put the kettle on.'

Oh, but it was a good feeling to be sitting there. Billy made it seem as if it was only yesterday that they had last met; there was no awkwardness, no moments of silence while they sought for common ground on which to latch their conversation.

Fred was fascinated to hear of the past as Billy resurrected it - a whole chunk of history that ought to have been part of Fred's life.

After referring to his sister Alma several times, Billy suddenly said, 'our Alma's still around. Would you like to see her?'

Fred smiled, nodding. 'If it's not too much trouble.'

'Trouble? Why she'll be that pleased...'

His sister answered his call immediately and Fred heard him say, 'You'll never guess who I've got 'ere with me.'

There was a pause, and Fred, watching, saw his mouth drop open. Slowly he turned from the phone to face him. 'She knew. She bloody knew, without me even givin' her a hint. Well, what do you make of that?'

What did he make of it? Was it just one more of those curious coincidences, or had she in some telepathic way been able to tune in to their thoughts? A spooky feeling raised the hairs on the back of his neck.

Putting the receiver back on its rest Billy heaved himself out of the arm chair. 'Come on, lad. I'll drive you over. She's lookin' forward to meetin' you. I told you she'd be pleased to see you, didn't I? I knew she'd be pleased.'

Because Billy had aged so much Fred had been expecting to find Alma with similar signs of wear, but to his surprise she greeted him with a vigour and youthful looks that belied her age.

'So you've come back,' she said in a matter-of-fact way. 'Come on in.'

Her memory, he soon realised, was in fact far better than his own. As he listened to her reminiscing she triggered off all kinds of memories he found lying dormant somewhere in the back of his mind.

'Now, have you been back to look at the Red Elephant?' she asked.

'What? Is it a pub?' he queried.

'No, don't you remember? It's what folk called the village hall at Holme Chapel 'cause it never really did prove to be the success they had once dreamed of. An' then there was the village hall at Cliviger, The Blue Pig.'

'You're pullin' my leg,' Fred scolded.

She shook her head. 'No I'm not. I bet you remember the times we used to go mumming?'

Yes, now she mentioned it, he did.

With faces carefully blackened by generous applications of soot, the children used to walk along the streets making strange humming, mumming noises, and then, choosing a likely door, they knocked loudly. The moment it opened the gang of kids would rush in past the astonished resident and with rags and a pot of black lead they proceeded to blacken the grate and polish the fender until they shone. White teeth gleamed from the round black faces as, with cheeky grins and outstretched hands they confronted the owner who by this time had followed them through to the parlour and had been watching helplessly their display of industry. There was nothing to be done but drop a penny into the grimy hands and hope that they left you alone, at least for another year.

A deep belly-chuckle from Fred set all three of them laughing. Those had been good days, hadn't they?

'I recall the panic we used to feel on those mornings when we stopped to play by the old railway station and we'd hear the school bell ringing,' Alma said. 'Do you remember, Fred, we had just five minutes to reach the playground before everyone had to file in?'

'Aye,' he smiled. 'And God help you if you were late.'

'But we never were,' Alma said. 'The distance between the old railway and the school could just be reached within the five minutes.'

'And often by the skin of your teeth,' Fred said, feeling good, enjoying so much the chance to reminisce with someone who remembered it all. He recalled hearing someone once say, 'when you no longer have anyone to whom you can say, do you remember? then it was time to be gone from this earth.'

Other thoughts took off like a chain reaction between the two of them and with many more, 'do you remembers' the hours flew by.

Suddenly she surprised him by saying, 'I always liked your mother, Grace. She was different to all the other women in the village at that time. I used to love the way she used make-up and painted her nails. Did you know that I used to scrub her front and back door step for a tanner?'

This bit of information was so new, so unexpected, that for a moment Fred fell silent.

'And I recall John Airey used to go to the club at Overtown playing billiards,' she continued. 'He liked at pint or two.'

Fred gaped. He could hardly believe what she was telling him, for all his memories of his adoptive father had been ones in which he had hated anything to do with alcohol. Could it all have happened after he was sent away?

'Where are you staying?' asked Alma.

'I thought I'd make my way to Roy Clarkson's. I'm sure of a welcome there. I met him back in seventy six.'

'I'll ring him for you,' she offered.

At the door Fred turned and shook her hand. 'It's bin grand catching up on everything,' he told her. 'Thanks for your time. You don't know how I appreciate it.'

'Well, when you see Roy give him my best.'

'I'll do that. Cheerio, Alma...and thanks again.'

But first he intended to take a look at the old house where the Clarksons had lived when he was a boy, where he had spent some of the happiest days of his life.

He drove slowly, wanting to savour the moment. But as he approached the East Lodge he saw, with a bitter feeling of disappointment, that the lodge had gone. A notice fixed to the gate instructed all would-be visitors to use the main entrance which lead to the Towneley museum.

That meant the long way round. Defeated he turned the car. He'd have to leave the museum until tomorrow. It was time now to make his way to Roy Clarkson's.

In what seemed no time at all he was parking his car and walking up to the front door. And there was Roy, round face, smiling mouth, exactly the way Fred remembered him. 'So here you are again after fifteen years,' he stated.

Later that night, lying on the bed in their spare room, Fred gazed at the ceiling, thinking. Everyone had been incredibly kind and helpful; without exception they had made him feel so welcome. He wondered how in the past he could ever have felt he was the odd-one-out, that he didn't belong.

After breakfast the following morning he set out for the Towneley museum. Following the route which lead him through Burnley he arrived at the official entrance. Inside the building he found the curator who registered immediate interest and attempted to answer Fred's questions. But there were no records of the pits or the mill which had once stood in Cliviger; it was as if they had never existed.

Was it possible that they were so unimportant to the folk who lived there that they had failed to find their way into the museum? Or had they been so common place that it had never entered anyone's head to keep records? Had no one seen them as part of the history of the area? To Fred it seemed unbelievable, but the fact remained - he had drawn a blank.

For two nights he accepted the hospitality of Roy and his wife Ada; like a thirsty man he drank in all they could tell him. He wondered if he would ever have his fill - would he ever be totally satisfied with the news of those in-between years they treated with such nonchalance?

Fred was in the bar of The Queen on the Saturday evening when a lovely idea began to formulate in his mind. It resulted in a long urgent conversation with the landlady. Was it possible? Would she go along with his proposal?

The woman, head bent, listened and nodded. Oh yes, she thought the whole thing was a grand idea, certainly it could be arranged. What a joke! Her eyes twinkled.

On Sunday lunchtime when Dave walked into the pub with his girl friend Janet, he saw first the back of a man behind the bar. Even before the exclamation of surprise and recognition had time to reach his lips the man turned and began to pull a pint.

'Dad!' Dave blinked and stared at his father.

'Morning, son. Be with you in a minute.'

Grinning to himself Fred completed his task and then asked, 'What can I get you?'

'You set this up, didn't you?' said Janet.

Dave was watching him closely, seeing his father looking happier than he had done for a long, long while.

'I thought I'd give you a surprise.' Fred laughed. 'I did too, didn't I?'

'Yes, alright then, you did. Now come out from behind the bar and I'll buy you a pint.'

Amusement danced in Dave's eyes. 'So this is it,' he commented. 'This is where you lived as a kid.'

'Only for two years,' Fred explained. 'Then my parents went bust, here in this very pub.'

'Does it feel strange?' his son asked. 'Coming back?'

But it didn't. It felt as if...well...as if in a way this was where he belonged.

Now he was up north Fred intended to take pictures of all the homes where he had once stayed. There were no longer any painful memories of which he was aware, only an insatiable curiosity. He planned to tour around recording Buckley Hall, Rochdale and St George's Home in Salford. But first, with Dave driving, they made their way to Fleetwood. Gradually gaining in confidence as old familiar signs flew past Fred issued instructions: 'Take the next turning to the left, that's Coniston Avenue. Now just drive down to the end of this street...'

The houses that had once impressed him with their neat tidy gardens were still there, and the avenue of leafy trees... 'Oh! Oh!'

Dave braked. 'What is it?'

'Look!' Fred pointed. 'It's gone. The Old Military Hospital has been demolished. It's been razed to the ground.'

They left the car and walked around staring at the site of the building that had once been Fred's home.

Dave grinned. 'Well here's one place you won't be photographing, Dad.'

'Looks like you're right.' He sighed. It had been a bad bad time for him there, but it was part of his history, he had planned to include a photograph of the place in 'the book', now there were only his memories to go on.

'When I was discovered by the billeting officer this is where he brought me,' he told Dave. But he had no words to describe the awful dread, deep in the pit of his stomach, that had accompanied him on that long walk, nor the shock he had experienced on entering the building to see the squalor, the peeling walls, the ineffectual single gas light hanging from the cracked ceiling.

Fred lead the way back to the car. He had thought there were no unpleasant feelings left but he had been wrong, for one moment standing there it had all come flooding back, stark and terrible. Now he just wanted to get away.

'Let's find Lord Street,' he said. 'I wonder if the Old School House is still standing?'

He hoped so. Oh, he did hope so. That place had been the back-cloth of many an adventure and happy times - despite old Nicholson.

The trams were still there rattling along the main street, but the front of the school had been completely changed. Fred viewed the building through the camera lens seeing, as if by magic, the building reduced to a tiny picture in miniature. If only all those years ago he had been able to look into the future, to have known that one day he would be standing here doing just this!

Inside they found that the Old School House had been completely refurbished and was currently being used for Youth Training. This seemed to satisfy something in Fred, he nodded at Dave, 'Okay, I've seen enough, we'll make our way back.'

Note: The Old School House Fred later discovered was actually called The Testimonial School.

By 4.30 they were in Burnley. Just before parting they arranged to meet up again in York. 'On Tuesday,' Fred shouted as Dave switched on the ignition. 'I'll have finished what I want to do here by then. I'll catch up with you on Tuesday in York.'

He watched Dave's car as it disappeared into the distance and then went to book in for the night at the Alexander Hotel.

Still with daylight on his side he climbed into his own car and headed for Littleborough. He'd taken a previous look at the map, aware of how much routes could change and how a memory of fifty years could distort what one would have sworn was fact.

He drove along the A671 towards Bacup enjoying the ride, anticipating the journey he would take through the beautiful remote forest of Rossendale.

Half way to Bacup the thought came to him to stop at an elevated point and take one more picture of Cliviger. He pulled off the winding road into a lay-by and stopped the engine.

For a long time he stood and gazed down into the valley. It was so green and peaceful.

'My beloved Cliviger.' He spoke the words aloud, surprised to discover he now felt this way about the place where he had so often suffered, been misunderstood and rejected by his adoptive mother. But for all that the happy memories, the fun, the good times, the love of John Airey were the ones that now kept him company; they mattered more.

Turning left on to the A681 toward Todmorden he recognised the route he had taken with his father on the bone-shaking old Sun motorbike all those years ago. It was still the same, dingy old Todmorden.

He grinned to himself as he drove under the bridge. Ah! There was the sign, 8 miles to Littleborough. What a strange landscape with its beautiful hills now covered with vegetation since the pit closure. But the black stone buildings in Walsden and Summit were unchanged - a grim reminder of the past.

Although the surroundings were not familiar, Fred suddenly realised that he was now probably in Littleborough. He pulled in to a garage for petrol.

'Excuse me.' He addressed the lady who came to serve him. 'Do you know if there is a remand home or institution around here?'

For a moment she looked thoughtful but then shook her head. 'I don't, but the boss is in the back, he knows this area like the back of his hand.' She turned away. 'I'll tell him you'd like to talk to him.'

Fred could hear the clicking of a computer keyboard; it was late in the day and he realised that the boss was most likely working out the day's takings. He hoped he wouldn't be irritated at being disturbed.

His expression for a moment was distant and discouraging as he looked at Fred. Then, deciding he was not a rep., he finally relaxed and smiled.

'I am sorry to disturb you but I wonder if you know of a remand home in this area?' Fred asked.

After careful consideration he said firmly, 'No, there is nothing like that in Littleborough.'

'Oh, well, thanks anyhow.' Fred made to move away, concealing his feeling of disappointment. He had felt so hopeful and now.....

The man's voice called after him. 'But there is a place near here called Buckley Hall. It's closed now but it used to be a high security prison for young offenders. That's the only place I can think of around here.'

Fred stared at him delighted. **Buckley Hall.** It had to be the same one. 'Can you direct me there, please?' He heard the excitement in his own voice and struggled to control it.

'Yes, certainly. Do you know Rochdale?'

'No, I'm afraid not.'

Gesticulating with his hands the garage man gave instructions, making Fred repeat them, anxious that now he could be of help he didn't want the effort to be wasted. 'Turn left, carry on for about one and a half miles, over the roundabout, then you come to a dual carriageway. About a mile along there you'll come to a pelican crossing.' The man nodded. 'That's Buckley. Turn right there and then it's best to ask again.'

Fred shook hands and thanked him. 'I hope you find what you're looking for,' the man said.

Parking his car just off the main road Fred climbed out and began to walk, hoping he would meet someone who could direct him. It was 7.30. in the evening. Time for Coronation Street, he thought with irony, that accounts for the quietness.

Looking up from the pavement he saw a young lady coming toward him. 'Excuse me.'

She stopped, eyeing him suspiciously. 'Yes?'

'I wonder if you know Buckley Hall?'

'Yes.' She relaxed a little. 'It's just over there. You go down this road for about a quarter of a mile and then on the left there's a lane which leads up to the hall. But you know that it's closed?'

He nodded. 'Yes. Thanks. I want to see it anyway.'

He drove slowly. A strange feeling of fear seemed to wrap itself around him, encompassing him like a dark mantle. What was there to be afraid of? The place wasn't even occupied. Still the feeling persisted.

Now he recognised the landscape, and passing through an iron gate the grey building came with forceful impact into sight. It was completely surrounded by a twenty foot high security fence.

Fred parked the car and locked the doors. A shudder ran through his body as his mind leapt back to that time when he was put in this place amongst young criminals and hooligans because there was no other place for him to go.

As he approached the fence a loud voice hailed him. 'What are you doing here?'

A small man wearing civilian clothing had emerged from behind one corner of the building. 'This is Home Office property,' he announced.

'I only wanted to take a few photos.'

'It's not allowed. Although it's closed I can't allow you to take photographs.' He came closer to the fence, suspicion darting from his small eyes.

It seemed ridiculous. Fred wasn't particularly tall himself but as he looked down on this insignificant person he realised he was helpless without his co-operation.

'I used to be in here. It was during the war.' He waved his hand at the fence. 'Before all this.'

At last the man relaxed, though for the life of him Fred couldn't imagine what he thought he was going to do that could be classed as threatening or dangerous.

'So you are one of the old boys, are you?'

Fred felt anything but pride as he answered: 'I thought that it was perhaps a remand home in those days, but I only spent three weeks here. No one ever explained anything to you.'

The man introduced himself as being the person responsible for security. Suddenly it seemed that he was glad of a bit of company, someone to talk to.

'This used to be a catholic home for waifs and strays,' he told him.

So that was it! That was why he had been sent here - while they found a place for him at Standon which was under the control of the Church of England.

For some obscure reason the man now relented. He proceeded to open the enormous chain link gates and told Fred that he could take two photographs. 'One at the front and one at this side. That's all.'

Fred obeyed. At least he would have something on record.

The gates slammed together behind him as Fred walked quickly back to the car. He heard the man locking them once more. He had said that Buckley meant Bleak House - how absolutely appropriate.

The fear was still there in his heart as Fred turned towards Salford. The thought kept returning to him: those few weeks he had spent there in Buckley Hall had been the most terrible in his life. Now, on coming back, in re-living something of those memories his feelings remained unchanged, it was still the most awful place he could remember.

He didn't bother to pick-up the M66 but travelled instead along the B6222 road to Bury, then on to the A56 Bury New Road, all the way down to Salford. Was it another strange coincidence that made he choose this way? As he passed through Whitefield, Stand and Prestwich he quite suddenly made the connection - these had been the names given to the dormitories at St George's in Vine Street.

Slowing now as he approached the beautiful tree-lined streets which he recognised as Kersal, he looked for the turning into Vine Street. Ah yes, he recognised his surroundings. But St George's, as he knew it, was sadly gone. There was no apparent reason why they should have torn down the old Home building and replaced it with this peculiar structure he found himself surveying: a mixture of brick and stone with louvred doors painted white. It must, he concluded, be some sort of office accommodation. An estate car was still parked in the car park. Perhaps someone was still working inside.

He walked briskly across the Tarmac, feeling far better than he had an hour or so ago at Buckley Hall. Climbing a concrete staircase he stopped outside a plain flush door. A notice claimed his attention: The Children's Society. It was the new name for the Church of England Waifs and Strays Society.

He pressed the bell and was almost immediately confronted by an affable man.

'I'm sorry to disturb you at this late hour...my name's Brayshay, Fred Brayshay. I used to be in St George's.'

The response was immediate. 'Please come in. You're lucky to find anyone in at this time of night.'

Another coincidence - it was as if all these isolated happenings were being pulled together, completing the fabric of the picture of his life. Setting him free, allowing him to go forward.

'My name's Peter Warburton,' the man informed him. 'I work for the Children's Society. Now, what can I do for you?'

'It goes back a long way,' he said. 'I'd like to find out what happened in 1938 and '39. I was evacuated from St George's then to Fleetwood with the Home boys.'

St George's Home in Fred's day

The site of St George's as it is today

'Really?' Peter Warburton exclaimed.

Fred realised that once again he was up against it - fifty years was a long time - too long. He looked at the man. He was no more than forty years old. He hadn't even been born when Fred's life was being moulded. From Peter Warburton's reaction he deduced that what had been a major event to Fred and the other boys like him, was not even mentioned in the society's records. A war had been on, no one had found the time to write of its effects upon the boys or their subsequent removal from the Home. It had simply not been documented or recorded.

He found it almost unbelievable. On this very spot where he had first encountered the disciplined but scrupulously fair ministerings of the matron there was no evidence - nothing at all.

Questions **had** to be asked and answers found. He **had** to know what had happened to the Home, to the boys who had shared his experiences. And what, indeed, had happened to Nicholson?

Peter Warburton was pleasant, he wanted to assist, and the offices were impressive, Fred acknowledged that, but he realised he knew nothing about the history of St Geroge's during the thirties and forties. There were no photographs taken during that time of people or events.

Fred left with a promise from Peter Warburton that he would do some investigation on his behalf. At least, he assured him, he would do his best.

For the purpose of 'the book' Fred felt it was essential he should obtain a photograph of John Airey. But where did he begin? Hadn't there been a club in Burnley where his adoptive father was once a member?

He seemed to be scratching away inside his brain, stirring up old and dusty half-forgotten pieces of information. There must be **something** that would give him a lead.

Now it came, slowly, bit by bit the memory surfaced - there had once been a Concert Artist's Club. Yes, he could hear his father's voice telling him of the stage artists from the Burnley theatres who would come to entertain, often for a small fee and free drinks.

His father had sung there with his rich baritone voice that commanded attention. Perhaps, if the club still existed, they might even have an old photograph.

Arriving back in Burnley Fred made his way to the Cattle Market Hotel and ordered a drink. There he asked the landlord if he knew of the Concert Artist's Club.

'Yes, I do.' He nodded. 'As a matter of fact the steward is a friend of mine.'

As Fred opened his mouth to ask about it a telephone rang in the distance.

'Excuse me one moment.' The landlord moved away. In a line of incredible coincidences it proved to be one more, for the phone call was from the steward himself.

'I had a word with him and told him about you. I'll tell you how to get there. He's expecting you.'

Fred walked the quarter mile to find this last relic of a different era surrounded by a completely new development of offices and buildings.

He wandered up the narrow staircase and entered a smoke-filled hall with a low suspended ceiling. To the right of him was a bar. Fred walked over and introduced himself to the barman.

'In a minute, when this 'house' has finished, I'll introduce you to the ex-president,' the man said.

Once the place of stage artists - where music and the world of artists had met - it had become a bingo hall.

'He's possibly the oldest male member of the club,' the barman was saying. 'He should be able to help you.'

They hurried now along the clearway between tables and chairs.

The man stopped. 'Tom, this is Fred Brayshay. He's looking for any information we might have about his father. He used to be a member here before the war.'

'Sit down, Fred.' Tom moved over. 'What did you say your dad's name was?'

'John Brayshay, but he may have been known as Jack. I remember he used to sing The Floral Dance. I wondered if you might have some photographs tucked away somewhere.'

Fred could see the familiar vague expression on Tom's face and experience told him that he had once more drawn a blank.

'Floral Dance you say. My, that's goin back a long time.'

Taking a deep breath Fred asked, 'Tom? Do you mind me askin' how old you are?'

He was sixty seven. Only a few years older than Fred, and they had told him that Tom was their oldest member. No wonder he couldn't recall his father.

'Eyes down for the third house.' They heard the caller for the bingo drawing attention back to the all-important game where hearts were made to beat a little faster, and where women, whose lives were sterile of any excitement, could be transported for a little while into a world of fantasy and dreams.

Tom looked up, an animated light shone in his eyes. 'The new president over there sitting by the bar may be able to help you.'

Fred moved over to the bar area and began once more to explain his mission.

But the man wanted to talk about the refurbishing. He had been personally responsible for it, he said. And for the painting too, he added.

Fred politely admired the work, wondering privately just how long ago all this had taken place. It felt a bit like stepping into a time warp.

After a respectful attentive silence he broached his subject again. Did they have any photographs?

'The old panelling's been thrown out.' The president's voice was slightly slurred. Was it always so? Or was this just a bad time to ask someone to try and remember.

'What about photographs? Photographs of the old members and events. Where are they?' Fred pushed harder, striving to hold his attention.

'Most of 'em, I think,' he said, speaking slowly and with painful deliberation, 'are downstairs.'

Encouraged, Fred asked. 'Can I see them?'

'I can't let you see them tonight.' He smiled weakly. 'To be honest I'm a bit upset because my daughter's car has broken down in Pontefract and I've had rather a few drinks.'

Fred's optimism evaporated. He stared blankly at the benign face.

'I will be happy to let you have a look any Saturday if you ring me to arrange a time.'

'But I only have tonight,' Fred told him. 'I'm leaving later for York.'

'I'm sorry to hear that,' the president said, and rising shakily to his feet he disappeared.

So that was that. Fred sighed. He would finish his beer and go. The whole thing had been a total waste of time.

But as he prepared to leave the president reappeared. 'Hold on a minute. I've just remembered...there was a couple of pictures in my office somewhere.'

Fred followed the president's unsteady steps through several doors and into an office. It was quite obvious that it had been used as a drink store during the refurbishing. What a shambles.

'There they are!' The president lunged forward. 'Under those boxes.'

Triumphantly he dragged one of the framed pictures out and held it up to the light.

It was about three feet square, dated 1903, and proved to be of a football team.

The other was dated even earlier. John Airey would have been about two years old when it was taken. Fred smiled to himself and thanked the man, but he wasn't listening; squatted on the floor he was investigating something else that now held his befuddled attention.

Quietly Fred withdrew, waving to the steward as he made for the stairs.

Clickety click. 'House!'

The sounds rang in Fred's ears as he drove back to the hotel.

He wondered whether the president would spend the night quietly snoozing on the office floor or whether someone would eventually realise he was missing and rescue him.

This 'going back' he decided was certainly a funny business.

On his way to York he decided to call once more at Bradley. He had no difficulty in locating Swale's Farm. A 'For Sale' notice was fixed to the wall of the house. It was no longer a farm but a private residence with the outbuildings converted into garages. There was no one to ask.

But there was no reason why he shouldn't look up Jim Brayshay. The cool, uninterested reception he had received on his last visit he decided to treat as a thing of the past. It was worth perhaps another try.

Evelyn Brayshay greeted him with dark doubtful eyes. 'He's just about to go back to bed,' she said.

Fred raised his eyes brows. It was ten in the morning.

'Can I come in for a minute?' he asked.

'Oh, well! Perhaps he'd like to see you.' At the foot of the stairs she called up to her husband. 'Jim, there's someone here would like to see you.'

He came, looking only half the man he had been. Slowly, laboriously, he lowered himself into an armchair.

'Whatever's happened to you?' Fred looked at him, genuinely concerned.

'I've had a bit of trouble with my back and shoulder but thankfully I'm getting over it. But I felt right poorly this morning. Evelyn thought I'd best go back to bed.'

'Then I'll not keep you.' Fred made to rise, but Jim's outstretched hand anchored him to the seat. 'I'd like to talk a bit. It's not often we see you around these parts,' he admitted.

'It's been fifteen years since I last came,' Fred reminded him. He was shocked to see such a change in the man.

Maybe it was the recent heart attacks he learned of that had caused such a dramatic change; it must affect a man, learning to come to terms with the frailty of life, in any case this time he showed such open pleasure at seeing Fred that he lingered there long after he felt he should have gone, once more listening and storing

178

away all he was told.

'I had to sell the business,' Jim informed him. 'That butchers had bin in the family for donkey's years. 'Twas Dad's, you'll remember, before I took it on.'

That continuity, the theme of endless procession through the years was what fascinated Fred and held him captive.

He looked at a box Evelyn had fetched at Jim's bidding. 'Old photos,' the man said. 'Now let's see what we've got that might interest you.'

'I don't suppose you have any of John Airey?' Fred leaned forward, peering at the faded faces; some he was still able to recognise, other's were long-forgotten names.

'I don't think so,' Jim said, and then with a cry he pulled from way down in the pile one that Fred instantly recognised.

It was an old fashioned sepia coloured photograph of his adoptive parents. There was Grace Mary sitting in an old fashioned dress with John Airey standing beside her staring straight at him. It was an eerie feeling, for there, right before his eyes were the two people who had each, in such in diverse ways, had such an influence on his life.

'An ere's one of yer Dad.' Jim handed it over. 'You can keep them,' he said. 'Go on. I won't need them.'

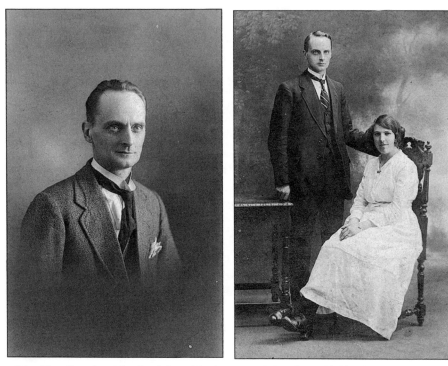

John Airey Brayshay Adoptive father of Fred   *John Airey with his wife, Grace Mary*

These photos were given to Fred by Jim Brayshay in 1991

'We went to see Grace several times when she was in hospital,' he said, nodding at the picture. 'She died a terrible death from cancer.'

Now Evelyn spoke. 'We went to her funeral too, Jim. Don't you remember?'

'Oh, aye. I'm not likely to forget that one either. I told you about yer dad's, didn't I?' he asked.

Fred nodded, he was not likely to forget either, the saga about the car door being smashed and how important it had seemed at the time to Jim.

He continued, 'Well, we went to the wrong place. You see we naturally expected Grace to be buried. She'd become catholic - or maybe she always had bin. Anyway, there we was at the church and then we discovered she was bein' cremated and we were supposed to be at the crematorium. By the time we got there the whole thing was almost over.' He sighed. 'Funny things, funerals.'

'Tell him about the restaurant, Jim, where we used to go when we went visiting Grace in hospital,' Evelyn prompted.

'Ah, yes! It was a long journey,' Jim said. 'So we decided to have something to eat and drink before we started back. And what do you think...?'

Before Fred had time to think anything, he went on, 'It was Ralph Mason's - still there. Do you remember it?'

How could he ever forget, or the hours he'd waited there for his Mam to finish work, to come home.

Note: He was to go back later to look, but by then the whole place had disappeared. A modern shopping precinct had sprung up with its busy people, some pushing prams, others carrying plastic carrier bags, those hurrying to appointments - once part of this had been Ralph Mason's superior restaurant for those who could afford to eat there.

'I can tell you where some of the Brayshay family are buried if you want to take a look,' Jim said. His voice was tiring and Fred knew he must soon take his leave.

'I'd like that very much, ' he replied.

'It's in Kirkby Malham, about fifteen miles north of Skipton.'

'Thanks, Jim. Maybe I'll take a look when I'm over that way.' Now it really was time to go. He took Jim's hand, holding it for a moment, grateful for all he had told him. 'Take care of yourself,' he said quietly. He felt a sadness, he didn't think he would ever see him again.

Meeting Dave in York was a relief. He was so down-to-earth, so easy to get on with. They toured the city, visiting the Minster, the steam museum, the golf driving range - doing all the things Fred used to dream, as father and son, they would one day share together.

The newspapers informed them that the races were on at Catterick. 'Tell you what, Dave,' Fred suggested on reading this. 'We'll drive to Ripon, leave your car there and go to the races together. We could stay on the night if we decide to and enjoy our winnings and then we'll go back and spend a night with Mervyn and Barbara. They're expecting us.'

They lost some and won some and had a thoroughly good day: now they were on their way back to pick up Dave's car.

There was still so much he had to tell Dave, so much he wished to show him. He wanted somehow to offer him a past, roots that he could also hang on to long after Fred had gone. This is my beginning, he wanted to say, I am what I am because of all this.

But something in Dave's eyes caused the words to fade on his lips. Softly he asked, 'What is it son?'

'I'm not going with you, Dad. I'm not going to Boroughbridge.'

'What do you mean? Why?'

'Dad, I can't. I...I don't want to. I'm going back to Taunton. I'm going home.'

Nothing would dissuade him. He was adamant. 'I don't belong here. This isn't MY past.'

There was nothing more to be said. With thoughts that reached beyond words Fred watched him drive away, and then, with an empty feeling, he went to make the phone call he knew Mervyn and Barbara were awaiting.

'I'm on my own,' he explained. 'Dave...Dave had to go back sooner than expected.'

'Well, get on round here.' Mervyn's voice, warm and friendly. 'Barbara says to tell you she's cooked you a dinner.'

The welcome they gave him created a glow inside him, helping to ease away the disquieting feelings Dave had caused with his sudden announcement that he was going home.

Beverley was there, this time with her boy friend. It felt as if things were as they had always been. After an excellent dinner Mervyn and Barbara settled down to tell him the latest news.

Fred sat listening: It's as if I belong, he thought. And now I'm back they want to share with me all that's happened during my absence.

'I'm on 'lates' this week at work,' Mervyn told him.

'So,' Barbara said, 'tomorrow I'm going to take you over to meet Louise, our other daughter, and her husband Eddie.'

It was one of those casual things you never expect to lead anywhere, at the time he didn't give it a second thought.

But, to Fred's surprise, he learned from Eddie that his mother and grandmother had both worked at 75 Allhallowgate in Ripon - the place where he was born.

What a discovery! It was as if some great map had been designed in a specific way to bring him here at this precise moment in time. To think that both women had at one time actually worked in that building.

Eddie said, 'I can get Mam on the phone - the old lady's gone, but mother may be able to tell you something.'

'Ask her if she can remember her mother working there in nineteen twenty eight - September eighteenth it was when I was born. Ask her if she knows where the babies went when they left the workhouse.'

Listening in to the telephone conversation, Fred had to work hard to control his rising excitement as the man spoke with his mother. It seemed ages before he finally replaced the receiver and turned back to him. 'She says her mother was there around the time you were born. She doesn't know much else but she's going to see what she can find out and will let me know.'

Fred leaned back in the chair and breathed deeply, almost he could not believe his luck. Now, at last, there was a chance that he could fill in those missing eighteen months.

When Fred told Mervyn and Barbara about his visit to Jim Brayshay's, and that through him he had discovered the family had originated from Kirkby Malham, Mervyn decided that they should visit the place and take a look for themselves.

The trip up into the Dales the following Saturday was a perfectly lovely experience.

'We should do this more often,' Mervyn remarked as they made their way from Ripon to Pateley Bridge.

There they turned right taking the narrow lane to Wath. Moving into a low gear the car made its ascent to Middlemoor. Finally they arrived at the awe-inspiring Scar House reservoir and stopped.

They climbed out to stretch their legs and Mervyn began with much enthusiasm to explain the extraordinary engineering feat. 'It was constructed in about eight years by a workforce who lived in a kind of worker's village right on the site. The remains of the foundations of the houses are still visible.'

Fred marvelled at the enterprise, noticing how low the water was. But he wanted to get on. He wanted to see that cemetery and they seemed to be losing interest in the idea.

'We'll push on to Grassington,' Mervyn said glancing at his watch. 'See what time it is when we get there and then make up our minds.'

But Fred's mind was already made up and he knew that somehow he was going to persuade Mervyn and Barbara to go along with his wishes to visit Kirkby Malham.

It was around four o'clock in the afternoon when Mervyn parked the car at the cemetery.

'Where shall we start looking?' he asked, seemingly now quite interested.

Fred pointed to a woman in her eighties tending a grave. 'I'll ask that lady over there.'

But she shook her head. 'I'm sorry, I've never heard the name Brayshay. I only come here now and again from Grassington.'

'Let's split up,' Barbara suggested. 'That way we can each cover a different section.'

The church yard was enormous, appearing to be divided into three sections. Ancient grave stones basked in the brilliant sunshine, some leaning precariously in the green turf. A restful atmosphere of timelessness surrounded them.

But it proved to be a difficult task. Ignoring the newer graves they peered at the weathered inscriptions, often having to scrape away the lichen and clinging moss from the worn stone.

After about three quarters of an hour they were ready to give up. It seemed that Jim Brayshay had been mistaken.

Fred and Barbara had re-grouped having decided it was fruitless to waste any further time when Mervyn joined them. 'It's no use,' he said. 'There are no Tews in this grave yard.'

Barbara turned on her husband. 'You silly bugger!' she exclaimed. 'We are looking for Brayshays not Tews!'

They laughed until tears appeared in their eyes. To Fred it summed up the whole situation - even his blood relatives became confused over who he was and where he really belonged.

Walking together now they went to explore the lower part of the cemetery.

'Here,' Mervyn suddenly called out. 'Here you are. There's hundreds of them.'

It might have been a bit of an exaggeration, Fred thought, but as he looked he saw that there certainly seemed a great many.

In one corner of the church yard a large area harvested the remains of Brayshays through the ages. Fred struggled to read the words carved in stone. The oldest one they were able to decipher dated back to 1705.

With a deep sense of satisfaction and achievement they made their journey back to Mervyn's home and then, for Fred, once more, he returned to Taunton.

It was the morning of Friday 13th September 1991 when Fred heard the click of the letter box and went into the hall to find a white envelope lying on the mat. Usually there were two or three uninteresting brown envelopes, but this morning there was only this one; it was franked with the stamp of The Children's Society.

This was the third letter he had received from the organisation since his visit to their offices in July. Although they had tried very hard to help him in his quest, it was obviously a difficult task to go back fifty odd years, especially considering that the second world war had resulted in many records being lost or destroyed; they had also confirmed that during this period photographs had not been taken or detailed records kept of the children in care of the Children's Society.

Fred picked up the envelope, feeling the thickness of its contents between his fingers. At a guess he reckoned there must be three or four foolscap sheets enclosed.

He placed it on the table and went to complete his chores; washing up, making toast, brewing up his usual pint mug of tea.

After completing breakfast he had a bath and made the bed. As he dressed he thought about the letter waiting on the kitchen table for him to open. Would there be anything new in it?

Eventually he went downstairs, put the dirty laundry into the washing machine and picked up the envelope.

Weighing it in his hand he wondered about the contents; there wasn't any more room in his mind for disappointment - it was far better not to expect anything, that way, whatever he found out now was an added bonus.

In the front room, small but comfortable, he finally opened the letter. Ah, but this was more like it. This was specific. As he made his first cursory inspection of the contents he noticed the references to Standon, the workhouse and a new name - St Christopher's Home For Babies.

Fred began to read carefully, digesting each paragraph, each sentence, each word.

Philip West of the Society had written:

Apologies for such a lengthy delay but we are now able to provide the following details from those records held in your name.

The earliest recorded details reveal that in March 1928 a situation was found for your mother, one in which she had remained until the following August. Elsie Tew then went to the workhouse where it was said 'The mistress found her to be a good worker and had no fault to find with her personal character'.

Fred paused in his reading; this dialogue was like something out of a Dicken's novel. He wondered what they had meant by 'finding a situation' for his mother. Did she work on the premises or in Ripon?

He sighed. 'Oh well! Let's push on with it.'

The next paragraph read:

Following Fred's birth in the Ripon Poor Law Infirmary he was baptised at Holy Trinity Church also in Ripon on 24th October 1928.

That made it exactly eighteen years from the day of his baptism to the day he had joined the army on October 24th 1946. How strange.

In the fourth paragraph he read:

It was noted that Fred was admitted into the Church of England Society's Care and placed in its St Christopher's home in Leeds on 22nd December 1928.

Previous to that it appears Fred was kept at the workhouse (presumably with his mother.)

Fred smiled to himself thinking that at least his first Christmas must have been better in the Home than in a workhouse.

The remainder of the letter only told Fred what he had always known about other periods of his life.

Thoughtfully he sipped at his tea. Now, finally, he knew what had happened to him from birth to his adoption in May 1930. So that completed his background - or did it?

He spoke aloud, 'I must try and get a photo of St Christopher's.' And then more slowly, 'I wonder what my real Dad's name was?'

A couple of days later he wrote to Mervyn Tew giving him this latest information. He wondered if Mervyn would be interested to learn these facts about Elsie Tew who had been his aunt.

Friday evening, about 5.30. Fred was just noticing how the nights were drawing in when the telephone rang.

'Mervyn here, Fred. Hello! I've got some good news for you.'

Fred settled down to listen.

'The fact is, we have received your nice letter... I have a couple of days off...'

Fred waited. What was it he wanted to tell him?

'Look, Fred...I'll ring back a bit later, about 6.15. I think we know who your father was.'

Fred continued to sit there, long after Mervyn had rung off. He didn't know what to make of his extraordinary phone call. He guessed he was going to ring back after six to take advantage of the cheaper rate. But surely it would be better if he rang Mervyn? In any case he found it quite impossible to just sit there and do nothing, not after being told something like that?

He lifted the receiver and dialled the number.

'Hello, Mervyn?'

'Fred? Hello. Now where was I? Oh yes! Since I got your letter I decided to visit Holy Trinity Church in Ripon. I spoke to the vicar there who told me that the records of all baptisms were sent to Northallerton. Anyway,' he continued, 'I've spoken to the records office and they have confirmed your baptism on the 24th October 1928 at Holy Trinity and those present at the ceremony were Elsie, your mother, and...wait for it... your father, whose name was given as Alfred, a soldier.'

'Did it give his surname?' Fred asked. A lump had suddenly materialised in his throat.

'Afraid not. I'll try and send you a photo of the church for your book and the lady said she'll send you a copy of the baptism records.'

'Thanks, Mervyn. Thanks a lot.'

'That's okay, Fred. It seems like this really is the end of the road, doesn't it?'

'Seems like it, Mervyn. I'll be in touch. Give my best to Barbara.' He replaced the receiver.

A broad smile appeared on Fred's face. All he had to do now was to track down a man called Alfred who was stationed in Ripon around 1927 to 1928. No problem! It was so ludicrous he wanted to laugh and laugh.

He guessed that every illegitimate child whose father did not want to be traced must have given his profession as that of a soldier. Interesting that he had attended the baptism. He wondered why he had then deserted Elsie and her son. Surely if he had been already married he would not have risked discovery by being seen with her at the church. This in itself was a mystery he couldn't begin to make sense of.

Why would the father attend the service and then abandon him? Had he intended to return and marry Elsie? Could he really have been a soldier who got killed?

Fred gave his head a shake, there wasn't any way of knowing. He could speculate all he liked but he was never going to be able to solve this secret.

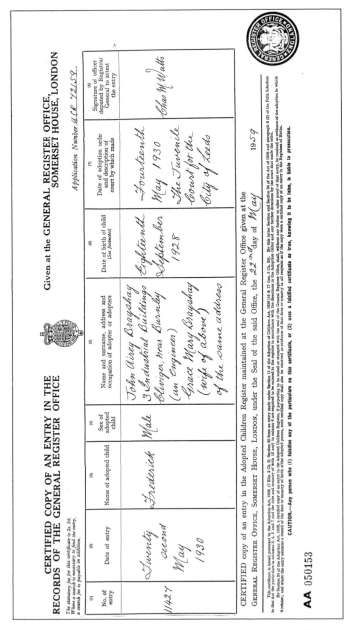

CERTIFIED COPY OF AN ENTRY IN THE
RECORDS OF THE GENERAL REGISTER OFFICE

Given at the GENERAL REGISTER OFFICE,
SOMERSET HOUSE, LONDON

Application Number ACR 721.59

No. of entry	Date of entry	Name of adopted child	Sex of adopted child	Name and surname, address and occupation of adopter or adopters	Date of birth of child (See footnote)	Date of adoption order and description of court by which made	Signature of officer deputed by Registrar General to attest the entry
11427	Twenty second May 1930	Frederick	Male	John Airey Brayshay 3 Industrial Buildings Elvington, nr Burnley (an engineer) Grace May Brayshay (wife of above) of the same address	Eighteenth September 1928	Fourteenth May 1930 The Juvenile Court for the City of Leeds	Chas W Watts

CERTIFIED copy of an entry in the Adopted Children Register maintained at the General Register Office given at the GENERAL REGISTER OFFICE, SOMERSET HOUSE, LONDON, under the Seal of the said Office, the 22nd day of May 1959

CAUTION.—Any person who (1) falsifies any of the particulars on this certificate, or (2) uses a falsified certificate as true, knowing it to be false, is liable to prosecution.

AA 050153

*This copy of Fred's Adoption certificate was obtained in 1959 prior to the
birth of his first son David*

Diocese of ....

Application Number 25316

Accepted Number 32,599

Name *Frederick* Braighay

Decision of Committee

Printed by the Society's Apprentices at St. Aldhelm's Home.

Documents and records held by The Children's Society from acceptance into St Christopher's Home in 1928 to discharge in 1945. It is interesting to note that Elsie Tew was to pay 7/6d per week to the Home, the rest being made-up by the Ripon and Wakefield Boroughs. Also it is shown that Fred's adoptive father made payments direct to a Manchester bank following his admission to St George's (Kersal)

When Baptised.	Child's Christian Name.	Parent's Name.		Abode.	Quality, Trade, or Profession.	By whom the Ceremony was performed.
		Christian.	Surname.			
1928 Oct 24th No. 1177	Frederick	Albert & Elsie	New	75 Allhallowgate	Soldier	Half Hicks Vicar
1928 Oct 24 No. 1178	Joyce	P Maud	Bees	75 Allhallowgate	Brightsmith	Half Hicks Vicar
1928 Oct 28 No. 1179	Josephine Ruth	William & Ruth	Fraser	Gladstone Terrace	Stallholder	Half Hicks
1928 Nov 21st No. 1180	Allan L	Raymond Appleton & Jennie	Ayton	Station View Ure Bank Sharow	Parcels Vanman	Half Hicks
1928 Nov 25 No. 1181	Phyllis	Christah Ada Prince	Skelling	20 Southgate	Woodman	Half Hicks (Vicar)
1929 Feb 24 No. 1182	Audrey Patricia	Albert Wharton Ada	Bake	23 Westgate	Bootdealer	Half Hicks (Vicar)
1929 Feb 6 No. 1183	Frederick Vivian	Vivian Margaret Elsie	Smith	4 Bondgate	Painter	Half Hicks (Vicar)
1929 Feb 14 No. 1184	Maureen	Henry & Annie	Linmann's	43 Princes Rd	Plumber	Half Hicks Vicar

Record from Holy Trinity showing Fred's baptism

190

Holy Trinity where Fred was baptised

*   *   *   *   *   *

Two days later Fred was putting the photographs he had obtained into an album in chronological order when his friend Mike arrived.

As they drank coffee together Mike became absorbed in the album, reading and re-reading the notes Fred had written explaining each picture.

Presently he looked up at Fred, and in a slightly embarrassed way said: 'You know, Fred, you'll never be able to prove it one way or the other...but I would bet any money you like that John Airey Brayshay was your real father.'

Fred shot bolt upright. He stared at Mike. 'What makes you say that?' he demanded.

'Calm down, Fred, and take a look at that photograph of you as a young man in Blackpool in 1949 and then look at the photo of him.'

Fred had looked, he must have looked a hundred times at John Airey's photograph, but he had never, not in the wildest moments of his searching, nor in the deepest depths of his wonderings had he made such a connection.

'His mouth is exactly the same as yours, even down to the dimple in the chin,' Mike said, pointing.

Fred studied the photograph for a long time. There was a likeness, Mike was right. Why had he never seen it before? He raised his head reluctantly and looked at Mike.

'You do see it now, don't you?' His pal was nodding, encouraging him to make the enormous mental leap, to at least consider the possibility.

191

Three hours later, with Mike gone, he was still studying the photographs. If this was true it explained everything. John Airey could easily have given a fictitious name, and as a soldier - well, no one would have been able to trace him.

Fred knew Grace Mary had been unable to have children, that was the reason given for adopting him. This latest revelation, if he chose to believe it, also explained why they had gone all the way to Leeds to adopt him, and why John Airey had been so good to him, spending so many hours teaching him things, making toys for him, why he had visited him in the children's homes, and why he had struggled to get him out again.

In a way it also made sense of why Grace Mary had treated him so badly, why she had often been so cruel, and had finally contrived to get him put away in a place from which there was no escape.

Not to be able to have a child of her own, and then to be put in the position of bringing up the one her husband had fathered with someone else...now he understood, he could even feel some pity for her. It wasn't him, Fred, she had hated, but what he represented.

An enormous burden which had been with him all those years slipped silently from his shoulders.

He sighed deeply, then quietly closing the album Fred went to make himself a mug of tea.

IN CONCLUSION

Information continued to trickle in from various sources. Photographs were unearthed by people whose interest had been fired by Fred's questioning and enthusiasm.

We felt it important that these pieces of information were added to the story. Details of the fantastic work carried out by The Children's Society, documentary evidence of what happened to Fred during the first eighteen months of his life, the work of Standon Farm School and the subsequent closing of the establishment and dismissal of Mr Dawson following the murder investigation are given below.

Information from The Children's Society:

In the 1880s some 300,000 people were officially classed as poor. There was no social security - only the workhouses which were overcrowded and squalid, and where families were split up.

Edward Rudolf, a Sunday School teacher, noticed that two of his regular pupils were no longer coming to his class - he discovered the boys begging for food on the streets. He determined to help them but found the Church of England had no answer. So began the 'Waifs and Strays'.

Children who came into the 'homes' were usually orphans or those who had suffered beatings, and some who had been sent out onto the streets to beg. The Society's first annual report states that there were 20,000 homeless children in London alone.

By the late 1920s and the early 1930s Standon Farm School had been formed and was operational.

In 1926 adoption became legal and the Society became an official adoption agency in 1935.

The work continued, helping not only the homeless and unwanted but also much work was undertaken to help disabled children and unmarried mothers.

In the 1960s the birth rate began to fall and the Society started an active programme for the hard to place child.

Despite the fall in the birth rate, 1967 was a peak year for illegitimacy and, in 1969, the Society opened a hostel for unsupported mothers and their children.

In the light of more than 100 years of experience, of continual growth and development, the Society now looks to keep the family together wherever possible, to work with the whole family, to provide support, help and advice where necessary, and to relieve pressure.

Standon Farm Approved School (known during Fred's time there as Standon Farm School):

On February 15th 1947 (two years after Fred left the School) a group of boys plotted together to burst in upon a monthly meeting of the Staff with Bren guns shooting indiscriminately and making sure to kill Mr Dawson, the Headmaster. However, due to the length of time they would have to wait in order to execute their plan the boys became impatient and decided to kill Dawson on the afternoon of February 15th and to rob the safe and stores using the Headmaster's car to make a quick getaway. Two of the boys stole some ammunition from the Headmaster's house during a dance which was going on at the School on the Friday evening. Three service rifles were stolen from the School Armoury. Four of the boys went into the ablution room and loaded the rifles. Another of the boys waited in the locker room which lead directly onto the ablution room. Two boys waited in the lavatory, one remained in the Armoury, one stayed in the garage with the car and the last of the group waited in the recreation room.

The plan was to be caught smoking by the officer on duty, knock him out and put him in the boiler room. But as soon as the boys had taken up their positions, young Mr Fieldhouse unexpectedly walked into the ablution room.

His sudden appearance caused one boy to panic, he fired the rifle and missed; reloading it he fired again and hit Fieldhouse in the groin, blowing out part of the abdomen.

Peter Fieldhouse lived about half an hour after the shooting and was able to give certain information about the boys.

After the shooting the boys panicked and set off across the countryside on foot through the snow.

By nine o'clock that night all the boys were in custody and the rifles recovered.

In the enquiry they stated that they did not intend to kill Peter Fieldhouse but were determined to kill the Headmaster, and if they got the chance they still would.

They were inflamed with anger due to what they saw as excessive discipline and injustice; their pocket money and licences, they declared, were always being stopped by Dawson.

The report stated: *At any time during the child's detention in an Approved School the Managers of the School may and, if the Secretary of State so directs, shall by licence in writing permit him to live with the parent or with any trustworthy and respectable person (to be named in the licence) who is willing to receive and take charge of him...*

However, the Managers in London did not review the progress made by the boys at Standon Farm School towards the end of their first year in the school - they left the 'licensing' of the boys to the headmaster. It so happened that Mr Dawson did not consider that one year was sufficient time in which to do any good to a boy and therefore did not review the cases during the boy's first year. This was the cause for much of the resentment amongst the boys.

A week before the murder Dawson had 65 boys in the school and had stated that they could not give any of the boys licence until they had more allocations as the school could not function properly with diminished numbers.

As a result of the murder enquiry the school was closed down and Dawson dismissed.

It was interesting to note that during the enquiry the building instructor had stated, 'there would have been no trouble if the boys had been allowed to smoke.'

Fred was serving in Malaya when he heard of the murder and the resulting dismissal of Mr Dawson. He felt that Dawson had been used as a scapegoat, and later, on reading the report was amazed to see how the facilities, discipline and routine running of the school had been presented out of all proportion to what they had actually been.

He is extremely grateful to Standon, for the opportunity it gave him during his time there, and for the constant support and encouragement shown to him by Mr and Mrs Dawson.

Fred does not believe we should blame our childhood for what we are or what we become. It is all too easy to blame everything on someone else, he says. As adults we must take responsibility for our own actions. Of Standon Farm School he still declares it was the best thing that happened to him.

Note: The report on the facilities of Standon which were emphasised during the murder investigation of 1947 states that the playing fields and facilities were poor but Fred sees this as 'looking for excuses'; as he remembers it the facilities at that time were better than most schools and he recalls them with pleasure and enthusiasm.

ACKNOWLEDGMENTS

We would like to thank the following for their help in making certain information available to us:

The Children's Society

The Adoption Officer, Harrogate

The Registrar, Harrogate

The Records Officer of Baptisms Northallerton

The Fleetwood Library

The Blackpool Gazette

Also our grateful thanks to Jim Brayshay, Roy Clarkson and Gladys Tew for photographs provided which appear in this book.

Mervyn and Barbara Tew for their constant support and research and for photographs provided.

Diana Jordon for reading the original proof.

Tom Gregory, for the many hours he spent helping to turn the manuscript into readable material and for his patience in explaining the mysteries of the computer and word processor.